APPALACHIAN HYMNAL

APPALACHIAN HYMNAL

Songs of Faith & Doubt

GARLAND WEST

Palmetto Publishing Group
Charleston, SC

Appalachian Hymnal
Copyright © 2019 by Garland West
All rights reserved

First Edition

Printed in the United States

ISBN-13: 978-1-64111-302-1
ISBN-10: 1-64111-302-2

TABLE OF CONTENTS

AUTHOR'S NOTE

O ver the years I've done a lot of writing, mostly for other people. But along the way, I occasionally tried to capture some of the odd thoughts and puzzlements that came my way as I stumbled through life. I never really thought about what to do with any of it, other than satisfy a basic desire to overcome my dull-wittedness in debate and abject failure as a stimulating conversationalist, as always through a keyboard. That's where I've always worked through some of the questions that have perplexed me about people, the world around me, and most of all, this brief moment of existence we call life. I'm not so pretentious as to think any of it is profound, or novel in any way, and certainly not on a par with the prose and poetry of some of the truly thoughtful men and women and elegant writers who have been and remain far more prolific and articulate and insightful than I. There's no need to start clearing a place for me at the Algonquin Round Table, now or ever.

As I recently embraced this thing called retirement and began putting my affairs in order, I took a day to read through the fat three-ring binder that houses my musings. I found no discernible grand message, or any really unifying thought or theme. But I was struck most by how much of it touched on the age-old questions about life and death, meaning and purpose, and the value of simple human decency – the same questions of good and bad, right and wrong, salvation and damnation that were drummed into me over the years in hours and hours of Sunday services in the small-town Appalachian South, in thunderous exhortations from the pulpit and sweet heavenly inspiration from the choir loft.

So here is my own personal hymnal for your consideration. Take it for what it is, coming from a seriously confused yet relentlessly bemused -- and often spiritually bereft -- old man.

You see, I've felt the pangs that come with old age and the knowledge that all the craziness and uniqueness of my experience will be lost forever in very short order, for good or ill. Maybe most of all, I suddenly wanted to capture at least some portion of it all for those who come after, for whatever sense or purpose they can make of it. And maybe, just maybe, it can somehow help others in finding their own answers to the questions inherent in these simple themes of all our lives. Something of every life should live on afterward, shouldn't it?

August 2015

APPALACHIAN HYMNAL

Amazing Grace

John Newton, 1779 (1725-1807)

1. A - maz - ing grace! how sweet the sound, That saved a wretch like me! I once was lost, but now am found, Was blind, but now I see.

2. 'Twas grace that taught my heart to fear, And grace my fears re - lieved; How pre - cious did that grace ap - pear The hour I first be - lieved!

3. The Lord has prom - ised good to me, His word my hope se - cures; He will my shield and por - tion be As long as life en - dures.

4. Through man - y dan - gers, toils, and snares, I have al - read - y come; 'Tis grace hath brought me safe thus far, And grace will lead me home.

5. When we've been there ten thou - sand years, Bright shin - ing as the sun, We've no less days to sing God's praise Than when we'd first be - gun.

AMAZING GRACE

An old, old story, retold and repurposed

I t's not easy, but I have to admit that one of the first things I check out in the local newspaper every day is the obituary section. I'm told that's what happens when you reach a certain age, either to see the names of the people you know who have shuffled off this mortal coil, or to make sure you're still part of the coil.

Whatever the reason, I was sad last week to see Bobby Stewart's name among the roster of the recently departed. Bobby was Denny Stewart's older, smarter brother, and Denny and I go way back. Way, way back.

Denny and I were in the same high school class, and we both went to the same college down in Winston-Salem. We also wound up in the marching band in both places. "*So you're musicians,*" people would ask. "*Nah, we're in the band,*" we would always reply.

Truth be told, Denny was a pretty fair trombone player. He gained a certain amount of fame in college – maybe notoriety is the better word – for standing out on the third-floor interior walkway facing our dorm's quad at 1 a.m. every morning, when the local AM radio station signed off with the national anthem, and playing along with the third trombone line, all with pride and real gusto. It wasn't even in the same key, but no one, including Denny, seemed to care. Like we said, we're not musicians. We're in the band.

Denny's real claim to musical fame, however, was based on the bagpipes he kept in his closet.

It seems Denny's Uncle Albert had discovered a real attraction to all things Scottish somewhere in the dim, distant past. His fascination with his supposed Scots heritage probably began with his life-long deep fondness for Scotch whiskey (and a serious lack of basic social skills), and grew from there. Somewhere along the line, Uncle Albert started showing up at family events, first with his fifth of Cutty Sark, then wearing a fine if too-short kilt of the bright red Stewart tartan and calling himself "Angus." No one remembers exactly when he started trying to talk with a Scottish brogue, but everyone agrees he sounded a lot more like Boss Hogg than Robert Burns.

The showstopper in this family theater came when Uncle Angus started turning up at family get-togethers, large or small, with bagpipes. First thing anyone knew, he would fire those babies up and start serenading the family and neighbors, mostly with what he claimed was his own personal rendition of Amazing Grace. Denny absolutely loved all this, and it showed. His folks recall him literally sitting at his uncle's feet at the back-yard concerts.

So no one was all that surprised when Uncle Angus started showing Denny how to play the pipes. Pretty soon, Denny could squeeze out several bars of what passed for the classic old hymn – at least, a version just as credible as anything Uncle Angus ever produced. The fact that Denny tried so hard seemed to make Uncle Angus deliriously happy. Or maybe it was the Cutty Sark.

But anyway, word soon got out that Denny Stewart could play the bagpipes. In and of itself, that probably was not news of earth-shattering import to anyone we knew. But Denny also played his trombone in one of the local Moravian church bands that made the rounds at Christmas time, tooting out a mellow kind of carol for churchgoers and sidewalk passers-by throughout the area, usually while band members froze their valve-stems off in the process. What made things fun for Denny – and memorable for all the rest of us – was the inevitable happy marriage of bagpipes and Moravians that ensued.

You see, once the church band directors discovered Denny could play the bagpipes, the wheels started turning. And when they found out his signature song – truth be told, the only item in his bagpipe repertoire -- was Amazing Grace, the die was cast.

Pretty soon the church people started calling on Denny to squawk out Amazing Grace at funerals throughout the local religious network. Funeral directors who worshipped Mammon far more than Yahweh as their primary deity started calling, too. For whatever reason, just having something as exotic as the bagpipes playing the hymn made people feel warm and satisfied, probably because they thought it somehow added to the dignity and elegance of the ritual send-off. Like Denny always said, it didn't matter that he never played the hymn all that well. Who really knows the difference between good bagpipe playing and bad bagpipe playing, he would say. Who could tell one from the other?

Denny wound up playing a dozen or so "dead gigs" each year during high school. Business dropped off a little when we started college, but the long arms of the religious community or the funeral industry would reach out from time to time to wrap Denny in their warm embrace and draft him into another performance. By now people were giving him five bucks for showing up and doing his thing, ostensibly to cover gas costs. Denny always called it his beer money. I always called it our beer money.

The pinnacle of Denny's bagpipe career came one fine late-spring day in our junior year. Reverend Sigmon from one of the Methodist churches in the poorest part of town showed up at his dorm room door one Wednesday night, armed for another battle between duty and indifference with the story of a down-and-outer found dead in the gutter on Sprague Street. Poor Buddy Bigelow had finally drunk himself to death at the ripe old age of 37, as everyone in his Yadkin County family had been predicting for years. Now they wanted to bring him home, and to give him a halfway decent burial. Just once in his life, the preacher lectured Denny, Buddy deserved some respect and real consideration, and you and your bagpipes are going to make that possible. Little did he know.

It didn't take long for Denny to surrender in the moral combat, even when he found out there just wasn't any five bucks to spare, what with Buddy being destitute and all the costs of getting his body back home and so on. What's more, it involved an hour-long drive up to and back from Yadkin County, and on a Saturday at that. *Well, okay,* Denny had said, trying hard to focus not on his lost Saturday but rather on how many more five-dollar deals this might help generate from an appreciative, debt-obliged man of God and his circle of friends. *Pick me up whenever you like on Saturday, and I'll be ready to go.*

What Reverend Sigmon said next should have been taken for what it was – not so much a complication, or even a warning or red flag, but an omen. An evil, evil omen.

You'll have to handle this one on your own, he had said. *I've got to be at an ecumenical retreat at Lake Junaluska this weekend. I'm leading one of the symposia on Faith in an Age of Republicans, so I have to be there. But I'll draw you a map to the gravesite. It's in rural Yadkin County, but you should be able to find it easy enough.*

That should have been the first sign of danger to any rational mind. *Rural* Yadkin County? As opposed to what, *urban* Yadkin County? Denny, to his later and lasting regret, let it pass and accepted the pastor's map, hand-drawn on the back of a Build Your Own Bong flyer that had been shoved under every door in the dorm the previous night.

He then tried hard – very hard – to put the whole thing out of his mind, and with the help of the bong flyer, largely succeeded.

Next thing he knew, it was late Saturday morning and he suddenly realized he needed to get rolling. So he put on his collared white burying shirt, grabbed Bad Betty (yes, that's what he called his bagpipes) and the map, and jumped in his ancient VW bug and pointed it northwest on Highway 67 toward Yadkin County. Plenty of time, he told himself. An hour and a half till the 2 p.m. ceremony. Plenty of time.

He got to Yadkin County easily enough, but finding the gravesite was another matter. It all looked so much the same. Nothing but fields and forest. Up one hill and down the other, round one blind curve and then another. No road signs, no markers to help. Just a bunch of pencil squiggles and a big X on a wrinkled piece of paper. He kept driving in ever-diminishing circles toward what appeared to be the final destination marked on the map, but still none of it felt quite right.

It was just after 2 p.m. when Denny finally careened around one curve and spotted a gaggle of people standing on the hill on his right. This has to be the place, he thought – especially when he realized the entire group was gathered in a circle near a very big pile of dirt, staring into what had to be the open grave. He veered off the pavement onto the narrow shoulder of the old country road, jumped out with Bad Betty under his arm and sprinted up the hill.

He was a little surprised to see how small the group was – maybe a half-dozen men, all country people, with sun-stained skin and more than a little puzzlement, if not outright suspicion, on their faces as this strange interloper approached unannounced. Denny never really noticed that they weren't in the usual funeral finery. What got and held his attention was the sheer size of the concrete vault in the hole.

Most of the men were holding shovels, and it finally dawned on him that they were already closing the hole, and that he must have missed it all. Was he that late? Had he got the time wrong? Or was Buddy Bigelow so very alone that no one bothered to show up?

Did I miss it, he finally asked of no one in particular as he stared into the abyss before him. All the men looked to what appeared to be the oldest member of the group – clearly the respected elder and acknowledged leader, who in any southern social situation was obliged to provide the voice of authority and finality on any open issue or unresolved question. After some reflection, he spoke.

Son, you ain't missed nothin' I know of.

Denny suddenly felt a wave of profound sadness wash over and through him.

You mean nobody came for this? No family... no friends... no neighbors? Nobody at all?

They all stared at each other for a moment, as if they didn't quite know what to say.

No, sir, the elder man finally said. *We're just finishing up.* And with that, he tossed a heavy, fat shovel of cloddy red dirt onto the cement shroud already in place in the yawning gateway to the afterlife.

Denny stood in silence, taking it all in, as one by one each man started tossing shovel after shovel of dirt into the hole. Eventually, he gave a small shrug and turned to walk back to the VW.

Long after that day, Denny would say he never really knew what came over him then. But between that hillside site and the car, Denny started thinking about how wrong all this was. A man is dead. A life is over. And no one cares. This poor SOB never had a chance, probably. Who knows why he drank himself to death, or why there's not one human being who seems to care. But nobody deserves this. Nobody deserves to be so alone... so insignificant... so forgotten. And what the hell. I'm here.

Denny turned on his heel and marched with real purpose back up the hill. The men looked up as he drew near, and slowed their shoveling, even if they didn't quite stop. Denny pulled Bad Betty up into firing position.

Would you men mind, he asked as he began to puff away and the pipe's bladder filled to readiness. They stared at Denny, then at each other. They simply shrugged and with typical country eloquence still said nothing. So Denny started playing his own unique version of Amazing Grace to the poor dead man, the group and, most of all, to the heavens above. And on this day, something special happened. Something really special.

Denny told me years later that at that moment, he never felt more connected to life, or the cosmos, or whatever passes for God. This must be what the preachers all say is the holy spirit coming over you, he thought. He was one not just with the poor deceased Buddy Bigelow, or the small assemblage present at that time and place, but with all of humanity. He was part of everything that might exist to give his life – and the lives of others -- meaning, order and purpose. He felt real love for this poor man, and for all men and women, and for all living things, and for life itself. He was more than he had ever been before in his small existence, and more than he probably ever would be again. More connected. More aware. More understanding. More caring. More of everything.

And his music that day expressed all that. He played the hymn as he'd never played it before – timbre pure and clear, pitch perfect, phrased with a genuine feeling and boundless compassion beyond his ken… something rich in sound and deep in meaning amid the heavy sweet smell of the ripe honeysuckle and freshly dug earth and budding tobacco wafting through the thick mountain air around him that day. The notes didn't just hang in the sky. They became part of the heavens above, spreading across the Yadkin County hills and mountains like God's own pure unconditional love.

As he played, the group of men slowly transformed. They stopped any pretense of work, and turned as one toward the open chasm before them, slowly removing worn work gloves and sweat-marked baseball hats, folding their hands around the handles of their shovels in mute testament to the holiness of the moment. They remained transfixed for what seemed like forever, as if they, too, were hearing the voice of God speaking directly to them, long after the last notes of the hymn faded away across the distant hazy-blue hilltops and down the dense green valleys.

Denny stood mute for a minute after finishing, staring into the distance, totally lost in the moment. The spell didn't last, however, and he looked up and smiled weakly to the men as he snapped back to reality. He nodded silently before turning to walk back to the car below. No one spoke a word. No one made a sound.

He was more than halfway down the hillside when he realized that someone was coming up fast behind him. He started to turn as the group elder approached. What he remembered most afterward, he said, was the man's hand, resting ever-so-gently on his shoulder – a big hand, thick and strong from years and years of hard work, decorated with calluses and beads of sweat and flecks of dirt, but at this moment light as a feather from an angel's wing and as gentle as a mother's bed-time kiss.

Son, can I say something to you, he asked.

Of course, Denny responded.

I just want you to know how special that was for me, and for all of us, I suspect. It was something. Something really special.

Denny was embarrassed, but didn't want to make the situation any more difficult for anyone, so he just nodded and tried his best to smile, if only a little.

I just want you to know that, the man said again. He paused, as if searching carefully for his next words.

I've been installing septic tanks for 26 years, and I ain't never seen anything like that before. I never knew how important this could be to some folks.

It took a few seconds for reality to sink in for Denny. But when it did, it came with a kick. He was totally speechless, and could think only one thought. *Oh my sweet Lord, what have I done.*

The man patted Denny on the shoulder, with sincerity, before turning and walking back up the hill. Denny watched for a moment, then slowly shuffled to his car and drove back to the dorm, where he consumed a lot more than five-dollars-worth of beer that night.

That should have been the end of the Great Yadkin County Septic Tank Burial story, for all of us. But it wasn't.

The very next weekend, Denny was standing in the checkout line at the Safeway just off campus with his beer, bananas and baby aspirin, when without warning Reverend Sigmon materialized out of nowhere and grabbed his elbow.

I've been meaning to find you, he said.

And I bet I know why, Denny thought to himself. He was frantically trying to think of some excuse or explanation to escape the certain loss of his hopes of heaven, not to mention his five-dollar gigs. He never got the chance even to try.

The Bigelow family wanted me to thank you for what you did for Buddy, the pastor said. *They were so happy with the services. They wanted to know how you came up with the idea of staying out of sight in the woods, so Amazing Grace seemed to come out of the heavens that way. But how did you know how to time it so perfectly, so the music rolled down that hillside just as Buddy was being lowered into his final resting place? There's no way you could even see the grave from the woods on that far side of the ridge. And why didn't you ever come down and let the family thank you in person?*

Denny said nothing. Absolutely nothing. It was all he could do to project his humble face while hiding his utter astonishment.

You know, you gave Buddy something he never had in this life. You gave him something really special. You gave him respect, and one moment of beauty and dignity in a life that never had much of anything but defeat and pain and shame and ugliness. The only reason Buddy ever had to feel special was because of his problems, and his shortcomings, and his failures. What you did changed all that for the family. It really made them feel like his life mattered…that he counted for something after all, whatever his demons may have been.

Denny often told me how that day helped him better understand how much life is a mix of the good and the bad, of tragedy and comedy, of destiny and chance. Life is what we make of it – no matter what "it" may be. Hope within despair. Purpose among happenstance. Respect and meaning and the worth of every single life, all buried in a septic tank.

But over the years, as I listened to what Denny had to say about that special day, another simple truth – maybe a more important truth -- seemed to emerge.

No act of kindness, great or small, is ever truly wasted.

We live amid a common philosophy that, perhaps with cynical good humor, holds no good deed goes unpunished. But at some point, we rise above the cynicism and realize that quite the contrary is true. No good deed is ever truly or wholly in vain.

We are admonished by science-fiction experts not to touch anything when we time travel. A single butterfly crushed underfoot could mean a changed, quite likely horrible future – invisible and unknown, and perchance immeasurable in its consequences. Every action has the very real potential to change something, and perhaps to redirect everything.

Maybe acts of kindness live by the same principle. Their consequences ripple through time and space, too – only with an opposite polarity, where the center of gravity of our actions is skewed more to the positive side of life's equation.

Acts of compassion great and small, the grand and noble gestures, the passing random charitable impulse, even a momentary, singular instance of caring – they all matter, they all have consequences. Their effects may touch a single life, perhaps dozens or hundreds, and maybe thousands or more, for the better. We may not see immediately just how things are better, and perhaps never will. We can't always see them, much as we can't see the plaintive wail of a bagpipe's hymn, or see the common yet pervasive gravity that grounds us all to the planet Earth.

We can't see or touch music or gravity. But the wise among us know they are there. They are real. They are powerful.

Denny taught me that true wisdom – what many might call God's grace -- may be having the faith to believe the same about any act of kindness.

So right after I read poor Bobby's obit, I sent Denny an e-mail. I expressed my condolences, and passed along a couple of old, old stories about the mischief the three of us shared from time to time. And I invited him to drive up to a hillside in rural Yadkin County with me next Saturday, just to smell the mountain air, remember Bobby and Buddy, and maybe swap some lies and stumble onto a few more of life's truths.

He's already said yes, but with a warning. He's bringing Bad Betty. And I wouldn't have it any other way. I can tell already. It's going to be a great day. Something special. Something really special.

I'll Fly Away

Albert E. Brumley

Some bright mor-ning when this life is o-ver I'll fly a-way,
When the sha-dows of this life have gone I'll fly a-way,
Just a few more wear-y days and then I'll fly a-way,

To that home on God's ce-le-stial shore I'll fly a-way.
Like a bird from pri-son bars has flown I'll fly a-way.
To a land where joy shall ne-ver end, I'll fly a-way.

I'll fly a-way O glo-ry I'll fly a-way.

When I die, Hal-le-lu-jah by and by, I'll fly a-way.

MY FAVORITE UNCLE

A family portrait, painted by a child

My favorite uncle is my Uncle Frank. I never really thought about him as my favorite uncle. But since he is the only uncle I have, I suppose that makes him my favorite uncle.

Uncle Frank is my dad's older brother. Uncle Frank and his family live in a little house up near North Wilkesboro, N.C. I don't know where Uncle Frank works or what he does, since he always seems to be at home when we visit and nobody ever talks about his job or anything like that. I think he may have worked once at a furniture plant near Lenoir, but not anymore. I remember Dad saying a long time ago that Uncle Frank was a real good furniture finisher. But every time we drive up that way, all those old plants are dark and the parking lots are empty and full of weeds, and the gates are closed with rusty old chains and padlocks. Nobody works there anymore.

One time after we had visited Uncle Frank and we were driving back to Winston, Momma and Dad thought I was asleep, but I really wasn't. I was just sort of tired and resting, but not asleep. Anyway, I heard Momma say Uncle Frank was a hopeless drunk. I'm not sure exactly what that means, because I don't really know why Uncle Frank doesn't have any hope.

Uncle Frank is a big man, even bigger than Dad. Most times when we visit he is sitting on the screen porch in a wood rocking chair. He is always glad to see us, I think, even though he doesn't smile or laugh a lot when we are there. Momma always takes a great big basket full of food when we visit, so there is a lot of stuff to eat. But Uncle Frank doesn't eat much, and mostly he just sits and rocks and talks with Dad some and stares off at the mountains a lot while he rocks, like he is looking for something real far away.

Uncle Frank is strong, too. My Dad says so, and tells stories about when they were young and would work all day clearing the right of way for the power company back in Cherokee County and there-abouts. Dad says Uncle Frank could work him into the ground, and was always laughing and cutting up and full of it, even when times was tough. He's not like that when we visit, but my dad has never lied to me, so I guess it's so.

Uncle Frank might be strong, but he seems awful puffy to me, and his skin is kind of yellow. He always wears old-fashioned bib overalls and a tee shirt under them. Sometimes he is barefoot when we get there, but sometimes he wears big brown high-top boots with no socks. You can see a lot of his skin, if you try to look close or don't, and you can see all the little blue blood veins he has everywhere.

Mostly I remember how funny Uncle Frank always smells, and even more how his eyes look. There is this kind of cloudy stuff all over his eyes all the time. You can't hardly see what color his eyes are at all. I wonder what he sees looking through those eyes, with all that stuff in them.

My Uncle Frank has a wife named Lucille, but we all call her Aunt Lucy. She is a lot different from Uncle Frank. Not just because she is a girl. She is small and quiet most of the time, and she smells a lot like some kind of flower. Aunt Lucy always is moving around doing things. She picks stuff up and puts it away, and she always seems to be keeping things in their right place and people acting the right way. The house is real quiet most of the time, and I think it is mostly because of her.

Aunt Lucy talks with my mom a lot when we are there, and she is real nice to me. She likes to read me Bible verses, and I think she spends a lot of time reading her Bible. Aunt Lucy talks about God's will and His goodness and how we all will someday die and fly away to glory, if we live the right way. Momma told me to smile and nod my head when she talks about that stuff and just go on, so that is what I do.

Uncle Frank and Aunt Lucy have three children, two boys and a girl. I am older than all of them but Richard. His name is Richard, but everybody calls him Richie.

Richie is tall and kind of thin, and very smart. Aunt Lucy always talks about how well he does in school and how much his teachers like him. Richie can tell you all kinds of stuff about history and geography, if you ask him. He talks a lot to us about all the places in the world that he is going to see some day. He has told me four or five times how he is going to join the Navy when he is old enough and out of high school. I think he will, too.

Richie's little brother is named John, but we all call him Jackie. That's because his dad, my Uncle Frank, always calls him Jackie-Boy. I don't know why he does that, but he does. Jackie is kind of fun to be around most of time. He makes a lot of jokes and tells stories. But he also can be real quiet, and sometimes his jokes aren't really all that funny. Momma says we are going to hear a lot about Jackie someday. I guess she thinks he is going to be something special when he grows up.

Jackie likes for us to go over to McDowell Street and watch the high school boys drive their cars up and down. He says he will have a nice car someday. He wants one like the people up in Mimosa Hills drive in and out of the golf course. It doesn't have to be real fast or loud or even any color. Just as long as I can count on it to get me where I want to go, Jackie says, no matter how far away that might be.

Richie and Jackie have a little sister named Rosalie. Sometimes we call her Rosie, or Rose. Rosie looks a lot like Aunt Lucy, only smaller. She is kind of thin and small and has the same color hair as Aunt Lucy, except for the parts of Aunt Lucy's hair that are gray.

Sometimes Rosie will climb in my Uncle Frank's lap and rest her head against his chest and they both just sit there quiet and still. Sometimes she goes to sleep sitting there in his lap. When she does, Uncle Frank will run his hand over Rosie's hair over and over again. I've seen him sit there in his chair doing that for a long time, while he calls her his sweet little princess over and over again, real soft and slow, almost like a whisper. I guess he doesn't want to wake her up.

Rosie is always hanging around with her brothers and likes to be with us when we play. She doesn't say much, and she doesn't start things so much but is happy to join in whatever we are doing. I think she makes her brothers happy, and I know they love her a lot.

One time we were playing with some of the other kids around there and one of them said something mean about Rosie. He called her a retard. He was a lot bigger than all the rest of us, but Richie and Jackie beat him up pretty bad anyway. That kid went home crying with a busted lip and a big rip in his shirt, and I haven't seen him since.

Rosie didn't say anything when the kid called her that name, but she started to cry a little when they were fighting. After the boy left, Richie and Jackie put their arms around Rosie and talked real nice to her and we all walked back to their house and started laughing and playing again later on like nothing bad had ever happened.

I think Uncle Frank and Aunt Lucy had another boy once. I heard Dad talking about it one time when he thought I was asleep in the car. They had a boy named Edward who was real sick and spent a lot of time in and out of the hospital. It went on for a long time before God finally decided it was time for him to fly to glory. Dad says that's when the light went out of Uncle Frank's eyes. Maybe that's why his eyes are the way they are.

I guess my Uncle Frank is my favorite uncle, even if I don't understand everything about him. I know how much my dad likes him, and I bet he was a lot different and more fun back before a lot of grown-up stuff happened to him. Dad tells me not to think too much about that and just to be kind to him as best I can. I try to. After all, he is my favorite uncle. I think everybody needs to be somebody's favorite something. That might be in the Bible someplace. If it isn't, maybe it should be.

O Holy Night

Adolphe Charles Adams

O HOLY NIGHT

A Christmas eve from long, long ago

North Carolina Highway Patrol Sergeant Tom Bennett had far too much seniority to be working a 12-hour shift on Christmas eve and was way too old to be out on patrol during the worst blizzard in more than 60 years.

But here he was, nonetheless, sitting behind the wheel of the black and gray cruiser on Highway 70 while the heavy snow and increasingly wicked winds were making it near impossible to see, let alone drive anywhere. Something like eight or ten inches of snow already had fallen by dark, and the weather boys were saying the storm would go at least another 24 hours, with the worst of it set to hit between midnight and four a.m. Happy travels, Santa, Tom thought. We're both going to have a long night.

Tom didn't mind, really. The younger troopers all seemed to have families, and Christmas meant a lot more to them than to him. Ellie would be just happy to be alone tonight, he thought, baking cookies for the annual Christmas get-together at the church. And truth be told, he and Ellie hadn't been all that close for some time anyway.

Patrol on a night like this was actually a pretty easy job. Mostly he needed to drive up and down the interstate from time to time, just to make sure there weren't any emergencies requiring his help. So far everything seemed to be safe and secure. So far the road remained passable despite the storm, mainly because Jimmy Shuford and his crew were keeping the county's big snow-plow trucks running up and down, back and forth pretty much non-stop. Right now Tom was more interested in the 70 corridor. The old highway was the main east-west route back before the interstate was completed, and with the countless diners, gas stations and used car lots and other businesses that still dotted both sides of the highway, it remained the preferred route for locals.

Tonight, it was quiet as a graveyard. The locals may not be the brightest or most sophisticated people, Tom thought, like all those travelers on the interstate. But they know enough to get indoors and stay there on a night like this.

Maybe I should do the same, he thought as he spied the red At Your Service sign materializing into view. Tom could always count on Darryl Buchanan to keep the gas station open, no matter what, and to have a pot of coffee on hand as dark as original sin and as bitter as regret. Darryl was an old truck driver -- a small, tough, wiry man with buzz-cut gray hair and a lot of miles on him. After several decades of long hauls fueled by equal doses of diesel and bennies, he had settled in as permanent operator and custodian of the small, dirty station and its vast and unchanging inventory of motor oil, wiper blades, fan belts, cigarettes and Slim Jims.

Darryl lived out of a small room in the back of the station, with a hot plate, a cot and an old radio as his major assets and principal companions. He had no family that anyone knew of, but rumor was there were a few ex-Mrs. Buchanans spread between Carolina and New Jersey, all of them long ago moved on to someone else, or something better. Darryl no longer relied on the bennies, but he did take a nip now and then. But he was a quiet and pleasant drinker and at heart a classic good ole boy, and the truckers would still go out of their way to fuel up at the At Your Service and swap a few lies with a known kindred spirit.

Darryl was sweeping off the narrow concrete steps into the station when Tom pulled up. The snow pack made a crunching sound as he ground to a stop and opened the cruiser's door.

"Wastin' your time, Darryl," he said as he got out and put on his official broad-brimmed trooper hat.

"Maybe," Darryl responded without looking up. "But it's somethin' to do. Besides, you gotta keep movin' on a night like this or your joints get all stiff and hurt like hell."

Tom walked past him and went straight to the coffee pot sitting on the ageless burner.

"This fresh?"

"Fresh enough," Darryl said, pulling the glass door closed as he stomped his feet on the mat and walked back into the station's one main room to take up his usual position standing behind the laminated counter. "Besides, what do you expect for nothin'?"

Tom just smiled and started sipping what he knew as one of the worst cups of coffee in the known universe. But tonight, it was hot and strong, and on the whole it tasted just fine.

They stood there for several minutes, saying nothing, staring into the white waves of snow lapping around the station. Darryl's radio was playing softly in the background from the old man's room in the back, with one Christmas carol after another filling the room. When Tom recognized the tune of O Holy Night, for some reason he thought about calling Ellie to check on her and to let her know he was okay, and more so to alert her to the high likelihood the church get-together would have to be postponed for a few days. But he decided against it. She is a bright lady, he told himself, and she will have figured that out already. Besides, he just didn't want to risk having her go off on him yet another time about not seeing Alex again this year.

Tom didn't think of himself as too old-fashioned or too controlling or too conservative or too anything. But ever since Alex had left home to start school at Carolina two years ago, the gulf between the father and son had grown steadily wider and deeper. Tom just didn't want to hear about how wrong the war in Vietnam was, or how unfair it was that black people were treated so badly by the society that Tom embodied, or how selfish and shortsighted businessmen were ravaging the planet. Alex seemed to think the whole world was screwed up, and it was somehow the fault of people just like his father, if not his old man alone.

Tom just couldn't take that kind of talk, at least the non-stop complaints and criticisms, and calling the president of the United States a war criminal and a mass murderer had taken it way too far. Their conversations had become increasingly hot, to the point Alex just stopped coming home, and Tom wasn't about to follow Ellie's advice to call and try to patch things up. Let him get out of Chapel Hill and into the real world. Let him get a job and do some real work, just to see what that's like. Let that boy grow up some first, he still said to himself whenever he thought about it.

Darryl spoke up and broke the train of thought.

"What in the world do you think that is?" he asked, nodding his head toward the highway.

Tom peered intensely into the sheet of white outside the station's glass walls for a few seconds before he saw it. Yup, that's somebody walking down the road, he realized. Must be somebody stuck and stranded.

The two men watched silently for a few moments as the figure grew slowly larger and a bit more distinct. Neither moved as the figure walked steadily through the foot or more of snow already on the ground to the station door.

It was only then that Tom and Darryl could tell it was a young man, probably no more than 20 or 21 years old, wearing the Class A greens of the U.S. Army under a great coat caked in snow and ice. Once inside, he stood stock still, moving his eyes back and forth between the two older men before speaking.

"Would you gentlemen mind if I came in and warmed myself for a few minutes?"

Tom and Darryl looked at each other for just a split second before Darryl piped up.

"I don't see why not," he said. "But son, what in the world are you doing out on a night like this, and on foot to boot?"

The younger man took off his barracks cover and began to fumble with the olive green scarf wrapped around his throat and the lower part of his face. He had been carrying a small olive green ditty bag in one hand, but he wasn't wearing gloves, Tom noticed. No wonder he is struggling with those coat buttons, he thought. Those fingers have to be frozen solid. Patches of snow and ice began to crumble and tumble onto the station floor.

"Thank you, sir," he said. "I'm making a mess of your floor. I'll step out and take this off."

"Don't worry about that," Darryl laughed, stepping forward to grasp the coat's shoulders while the young man continued to wiggle out of his straightjacket. "This floor has seen a lot worse than a little water on it. And I've got a mop that can handle anything you throw at it."

Once the coat was off, Tom quickly recognized the two chevrons on the jacket sleeve, and the combat infantry badge and two rows of ribbons on its chest. He saw the distinctive yellow of the Vietnam service ribbon but couldn't make out the others before the young man turned and obscured his line of sight. All he could see now was a dark wet spot on the jacket's right side, no doubt where some snow had gotten through the overcoat.

"My name is Sgt. Tom Bennett, and this fine physical specimen is Darryl Buchanan," Tom said, looking the young soldier up and down. "Who are you, and where are you headed?"

"Sir, my name is Robert Simmons," the soldier replied without hesitation. "I'm a corporal in the Army. I'm on leave and on my way home for Christmas. My wife is living at her parents' place out past Longview. I'm going there."

"On foot?" Tom asked. "Your car stuck somewhere? Or don't you have a car?"

"No sir, I don't."

"Then how do you expect to get to Longview in this weather? That's got to be eight or nine miles, maybe more. You're not going to walk it in this storm, that's for sure."

"Yes sir, I can. And I will."

"Corporal Simmons, that's not going to happen. You'd be a lot better off waiting this out till you can make that trip safely."

The young soldier didn't say anything at first. He simply stared Tom straight in the eye, and after a moment spoke quietly but firmly.

"Sir, with all due respect, that isn't your decision to make."

Tom didn't bristle. He had heard far worse than this over the years. "I could make it my decision, young man," he said in his best trooper voice.

"Maybe you could, but you won't," the young soldier said. "You've got a lot more to worry about tonight than me. And you're not about to keep a man away from his family on Christmas. Besides, you know I can do it. I've done things a lot tougher than walking, even in bad weather. I figure I can make three miles an hour or better in full pack, so I'll be home in four hours, max."

Tom didn't say anything. The young soldier went on, as if to prove his argument.

"Look, sir, I've already got this far," he said. "I started out on a bus from Bragg going to Hickory, but they stopped in Greensboro and said the roads were getting too bad to go on. I managed to catch a ride down 40 with a Roadway driver who was headed home to Conover. The guy was nice enough to go out of his way to drop me on 70 near the old bowling alley, and I made it here from there in not much more than two hours."

He paused to let his words sink in.

"That should prove I can do it. Sir, you don't have to worry about me."

Tom stayed quiet, but he could sense Darryl staring a hole through him waiting for his next words. The young soldier started again before he could speak.

"Sir, I have a new son waiting for me at my in-laws' house who I've never seen. It would mean a lot to me to be able to be there for his first Christmas."

"All the more reason to make sure you get there safely," Tom said. He paused long enough to make sure the young solider recognized the voice of authority. But he chose not to press the issue any more.

"Well, just make sure you are warm clean through before we make a final decision, and let's see if we can find some kind of hot food for you," Tom said. "When was the last time you ate anything?"

Darryl didn't know exactly how to respond. He'd never seen Tom back down on anything – ever. But it sure sounded like he was about to do just that. He turned toward his back room before he spoke up.

"How 'bout some canned ravioli?" he asked over his shoulder. "Got some big cans of it here somewhere, and the hot plate works fine. I know for a fact it will fill you up real good."

"Sir, I appreciate the offer, but you don't need to go to that kind of trouble," the young solider replied. "And I don't want to be beholding. I was sort of planning on eating when I get home anyway."

"You mean you're too good to share food with me?" Darryl knew how to play the game, too.

The young soldier blushed beet red. "No sir, not at all. It's just that I don't want to be beholding."

For the first time, he broke direct eye contact when he spoke. "And I don't have any extra money to pay for it. I want to use all I got for my son's Christmas present. It's his first Christmas, and my first Christmas as a daddy. I have to take care of that before I start worrying about my appetite."

"Shit," Darryl shot back. "I ought to have to pay you to eat this stuff. So don't say anything more about it. Make it my Christmas present to you."

"Thank you, sir," the young soldier said. He paused for a moment before asking, "Is there somewhere I could wash up a bit?"

"The crapper's that door right there," Darryl said, pointing to his left. "It ain't fancy, but the water's hot and the commode flushes. Most of the time, anyway."

The young soldier nodded and moved to the bathroom door with his small bag in hand. Tom thought it was a little odd that he would take the bag with him. Been a cop way too long, way too suspicious, he told himself.

After 10 minutes and no sign of the young soldier, however, Tom's curiosity got the better of him. He walked quietly to the bathroom door and turned the knob slowly and silently as he entered.

The young soldier was standing at the bathroom mirror, coat and shirt off, with his right arm raised high over his head. He was twisted at the waist, apparently trying to wipe his side with a mass of wet towels.

It took a moment before Tom grasped what he was seeing. The young soldier was trying to clean dried blood from the area surrounding what looked like a dozen or so stitches in his right side – closer to his back, really. Another half-dozen smaller red spots dotted his side and torso, but none of them seemed to be leaking.

The young solider didn't see Tom at first. He was too busy trying to get at the wound, and too distracted by the pain and annoyed by his inability to reach what he wanted to reach.

Tom finally spoke up. "You want some help with that?"

His words startled the young soldier, and he blushed – again.

"That's all right sir, I can handle it," he said.

"I know you can, son, but if you let me help we can get it attended to a lot faster and probably a lot better than you can on your own."

The young solider thought about it for a moment. "Well, sure, if you don't mind."

"I don't mind at all," Tom replied. He took a handful of paper towels from the edge of the basin, and soaked them in hot water and the pink soap always resident in the bathroom dispenser. He began slowly wiping way the dried blood, with special effort not to hurt the young soldier any more than he had to.

"What happened?" he asked calmly as he wiped the area down.

"It's nothing, really," the young soldier said. "Mostly shrapnel. Our patrol got caught in a firefight and took a few hits. Only one that's halfway serious was the one you're trying to clean up. A ricochet round got me, and they had to go in and pull it out. Wasn't deep, really, but it was tumbling when it hit me and they had to put in a few stitches to close it up." He paused.

"Some of my buddies got it a lot worse than me," he added absently. "A lot worse."

Tom kept wiping, in silence.

"It's not bad at all, really," the young soldier went on. "I just have to keep it clean to avoid infection, the doctor said. I think I pulled out one of the stitches getting out of the truck in Conover, so I just wanted to check it out before I get moving again."

Tom stopped wiping and walked to the door. He opened it and called out to Darryl.

"Hey, Darryl," he yelled.

"What you want?"

"Do you have any alcohol or peroxide or anything like that around here?"

"I dunno. I think so. Give me a minute."

Darryl soon appeared at the doorway with a bottle of rubbing alcohol bearing a label probably dating back to World War II. "This do ya?"

"Yup, it'll do," Tom responded. As he took the bottle, he saw Darryl's eyes widen as he stood in the bathroom doorway and got an eyeful of the young soldier's wounds.

"Christ, Tom, is he okay?" he asked with genuine concern.

"Oh, I think so," Tom said. "I'm no doctor, but it sure looks to me like he's had some good medical attention already. I just want to make sure none of that gets undone."

The young soldier didn't blink as Tom doused all the wounds with alcohol and tried hard not to flinch as he taped clean bandages from the ditty bag to each one. Tom tried to make small talk to distract him, as best he could.

"What's your wife's name?"

"Sandy," he responded. "Used to be Sandra Willis. Her folks are Peter and Jo Anne Willis. They live on the old family place on Henry River, off Wyatt's Ferry Road."

The young solider watched Tom's hands as he doused another bandage with alcohol.

"Our baby is Robert Simmons, Jr.," he said. "We're going call him Robert, not Bobby."

"What about your folks?" Tom asked.

"Don't have any," the young soldier replied flatly. "Momma had a bad heart all her life and died when I was twelve. Dad never really got over it and died right after I finished high school. Doctors said it was his liver."

He winced, slightly.

"I never had any brothers or sisters."

Tom tried to keep him talking as he applied the final bandage.

"You stationed at Bragg?"

"No sir, I was there for about ten days getting some treatment at the base hospital when my promotion to E-4 and the leave orders came through," the young soldier said in a matter-of-fact tone. "I was just lucky it all happened like it did, I guess. Once my leave is up, I go back to my unit in Nam. Got another five months on my tour, then I rotate back to the States. No idea where that will be, though."

"Good for another 3,000 miles," Tom said, tapping the young soldier on the shoulder. "Get your shirt on and let's have some food."

Tom walked through the station's main room directly to his cruiser and picked up the radio. Once he had checked in and repeated his location and status, he tried to sound casual in his next words.

"Larry, do you know where Jimmy Shuford is?"

"He checked in about 20 minutes ago from exit 126," Larry came back. "You need him?"

"Nothing important," Tom said. "But have him get back to me when he can. Tell him where I am and ask him to swing by if he can on his way back toward Newton."

He sat in the cruiser watching Darryl serve up ravioli on paper plates with two badly mismatched plastic spoons. Lord knows where Darryl came up with those, he thought. And my gosh, look at that boy eat that stuff. Bet he hasn't eaten since he left Fayetteville.

In a few minutes Tom saw the two big snow-plow trucks plodding slowly down 70 in his direction. They pulled into the At Your Service lot and the drivers left the engines running as they headed for the station. Tom knew they probably needed some of Darryl's coffee and would use his call as the excuse they needed to stop for a couple of minutes for a well-deserved and no doubt long-overdue break.

Jimmy Shuford was a local from one of the most extended families in the area. Shufords were everywhere in this part of the world, and Jimmy knew just about anything you needed to know about the surrounding three-county region. He knew who was who, who hated who, and more important, why. He knew where to find whatever you needed, how to get anywhere as fast as possible, and a whole lot more. He was the perfect man for his job – knowledgeable, smart, loyal to his community.

Tom liked Jimmy a lot, and he felt for him. They had been in school together years ago, and Tom had watched Jimmy court and wed his wife Sarah, and raise his three kids. He remembered how proud Jimmy had been when his oldest boy Terry was the first in the area to sign up once the war had escalated, and how devastated he was when Terry was also one of the first to die in that place so far from home. Tom had driven the lead car in the funeral procession carrying Terry to his final resting place up in Hibriten.

Jimmy's junior partner tonight was Randall Travers, known to all for reasons unknown as "Skeets." Skeets wasn't the brightest bulb in the string of local luminaries, but he was a good boy at heart and he worked hard and did whatever Jimmy told him to do without question. Since graduating from high school about five years ago, he had worked for the county operating and maintaining machinery, and absolutely loved the heavy equipment. Most likely, Skeets would view the assignment to drive one of the oversized snow-plow trucks up and down the highway non-stop for 24 hours straight as the best Christmas present he could ever hope for.

Jimmy saw Tom in the cruiser and headed straight for him. He moved slowly in his bulky canvas Carhartt jump suit, and the brown knit cap he wore continuously in winter already had its own crust of ice.

"Whatcha need, Tom?" he asked, with his usual directness.

"Got someone I want you to meet, and then I'm going to ask you a favor," Tom responded, opening the cruiser door as he spoke. "Come on in here a minute."

No one but Tom would have noticed Jimmy's reaction when he saw the young soldier standing in front of him. For a split second,

Jimmy's face seemed to go just a little bit pale before he re-asserted his usual self-control.

"Jimmy, this is Corporal Robert Simmons," Tom said. "Corporal, this is Mr. James Shuford. He's in command of that fleet of impressive vehicles you see in the parking lot tonight."

"It's my honor, sir," the young soldier said, extending his hand.

"No, I suspect the honor is really mine," Jimmy said back to him as he pulled the knit cap from his head. He waited a beat before going on. "What are you doing hanging out with these two?"

"I'm headed home on leave, sir. I'm going to spend Christmas with my family."

"That's good," Jimmy said. "Christmas should be all about family."

The room dissolved into infrequent but polite small talk as Jimmy and Skeets helped themselves to Darryl's coffee. Jimmy discreetly found a way to pull Tom aside in one of the service bays.

"So what is this all about, Tom?"

"We're going to get that boy home where he belongs, that's what it's all about," Tom said. "And I need you to make it happen."

"And how am I going to do that?"

"You're going to plow us a path to Longview."

Jimmy snorted.

"Tom, you know I can't do that. It's just me and Skeets to keep 30 miles of interstate open, and it's snowing an inch an hour… maybe more… and drifting like I've never seen before. Some of those gusts are 35 miles an hour, if you haven't noticed."

"So isn't the road to Longview part of your territory, too? And who is gonna know whether you plowed the damn interstate ten minutes ago or an hour ago, if it's as bad as you say it is?"

Jimmy just stared into space and said nothing.

"Besides," Tom went on, "that young man has made it clear he's going home, and going home tonight, even if he has to walk every step of the way. Jimmy, he's already hiked all the way from Claremont through this shit, and with a bullet hole in him. And to me, he's got a pretty good reason for doing it. He's got a wife and a baby boy he's never seen waiting for him just a few miles down this road, and by God Almighty I'm going to make sure he spends Christmas with them, even if I have to carry him piggyback myself the whole way."

Jimmy stayed still and quiet for what seemed to Tom like forever. Finally, he looked up and spoke so quietly Tom almost didn't hear him.

"So where exactly in Longview is he headed?"

Tom sighed. "It's the Willis family house. They live off the old Wyatt's Ferry Road somewhere down toward Henry River. He can tell us exactly where."

"That ain't Longview at all," Jimmy said. "I know about the Willis family, and they live off Wyatt's Ferry all right. But that's Hildebran, not Longview. It's a yellow frame house set back off the road about 100 yards."

"I don't care if it's Marion," Tom said. "We're getting that boy home, and the sooner we quit jawin' the sooner we both can get back to work."

With that, both men fell silent, standing stock still lost in their thoughts. The silence lasted no more than a minute, and probably a lot less than that, before Jimmy pulled the knit cap back on his head and turned abruptly toward the door.

"Get in your car and try to keep up," he muttered over his shoulder.

Tom walked back to the main room of the station and tried his best to act casual.

"Well, corporal, you all set to go?"

"Yes, sir, I sure am," the young soldier replied. He turned immediately for his coat and looked around for his ditty bag. "I just want to thank all of you gentlemen for being so kind to me tonight. I really appreciate everything you've done to help me out. I won't forget it."

"Ah, it's nothing, really," Tom said. "Nothing any halfway decent person wouldn't do for another. Especially on a night like this."

Tom put out his hand to the soldier, who shook it energetically.

"Tell you what," Tom added as innocently as he could. "I have to get back on patrol, so why don't I drive you down to the community college as I head out. That should save you more than a mile."

"Sir, you've already done more than I have any right to expect," the young soldier said. "I can't let you do any more than you already have."

"It's nothing, really," Tom said. "I have to head that way anyway, and my job is to serve the public. I believe you're part of the public, aren't you?"

"Well, if it's like that, I sure won't turn it down," the young soldier said.

"Then let's get going," Tom said, taking the young soldier by the arm and leading him toward the cruiser. He nodded at Jimmy, knowingly.

"Thank you all again," the young soldier repeated to the group.

"Merry Christmas, son," Darryl said softly. Skeets was locked in his own private conversation with Jimmy, and just nodded toward the young soldier as a good-bye.

Neither Tom nor the young soldier said anything as the cruiser crawled out of the At Your Service lot and began creeping westward on 70. Jimmy and Skeets had already pulled out ahead of them. The weather was getting worse, just as they had said it would. The wind was biting cold, and the snow seemed heavier than ever as it swirled in the streetlights and twirled across the high beams of the snow plow trucks. Most of the time, you were lucky if you could see ten feet ahead.

They were barely making 15 miles an hour from the get-go. But they kept moving ahead, and that's what counted most, Tom said to himself over and over as the plows sent a steady stream of huge sheets of snow into furious winds and the general vicinity of the highway shoulders.

The young soldier was so lost in his thoughts that he almost didn't notice as they drove past the campus entrance.

"Sir, you just passed the college," he said. Tom said nothing, staring ahead at the road.

"Sir, you don't have to do this," the young soldier said. "Please."

He waited for a response, and got none.

"Please, sir."

More quiet.

"Please."

He finally gave up and joined Tom in staring silently straight ahead.

It took Jimmy and Skeets almost an hour to wind their way off 70 and through a series of backroad twists and turns to the Wyatt's Ferry Road. The closer they came to the Willis place, the more the young soldier began to fidget. He's going to hyperventilate if we don't get there pretty soon, Tom said to himself.

They both saw the light from the Willis house through the blowing snow at the same time. Jimmy was right. The house was set back at least a hundred yards from the road, just like he had said. But that didn't stop Jimmy and Skeets from turning into the vague outline of a driveway in the drifting snow and plowing as close to the house as they could get.

They hadn't come to a complete stop before the front door of the house swung open and a middle-aged man walked out to see what in the world was going on. He took a few steps toward the trucks but stopped dead in his tracks when he saw Tom's cruiser pull up close behind them. The young soldier was out the car's door before the cruiser came close to stopping, sprinting toward the house as best he could through the snow.

When the man recognized who the uniformed figure was, he didn't show any real emotion, not even a smile. He obviously knew Bobby immediately, but beyond that simple recognition he clearly was struggling to take in such an unexpected scene.

Another figure had materialized in the doorway, unnoticed to all but Tom. The young woman stepped forward into the storm, slowly. She seemed so small to Tom, and her flannel robe was nowhere near enough for this kind of weather.

The light from the single bare bulb above the spartan porch played with the snowflakes and ice crystals dancing frenetically in the wind, producing a constantly changing shimmer and sheen behind the young woman. She didn't seem so much to be illuminated as wrapped in a halo of some kind. The simple beauty of that image washed over Tom like a warm shower, and for the first time all night he felt a sense of satisfaction. Maybe not actual happiness, since he couldn't remember having experienced that particular emotion in quite a while, and probably had forgotten how it was supposed to feel. But he was content, and that felt pretty good to him right now.

The image didn't last long, though. The young woman had recognized her husband immediately, and she launched herself at him through the wind and the snow even before he was halfway to the porch. Some kind of keening shriek cut through the wind, and Tom honestly couldn't tell if it originated with the storm or the woman. No matter.

Tom exited the cruiser and nodded toward the middle-aged man. Jimmy and Skeets crunched their way slowly through the snow to join them, no one wanting to intrude on the intimate scene unfolding in front of them. The young solider and his wife stayed locked together in the cold and wind and snow, saying nothing aloud but somehow saying everything that needed to be said to each other. The only sounds were the irregular wails of the wind and the idling clatter of the big diesel engines in between.

At last a somewhat dowdy middle-aged woman appeared in the doorway, wiping her hands on a kitchen towel as she took in the scene before her. After a few seconds, she took charge.

"You two get in this house, and get in it right now," she said as loudly as she could into the storm, but without any real anger or threat in her voice. "This is no time to go catching your death. You can do all that inside where it's warm, and I suspect you'll enjoy it just as much. Maybe more."

The middle-aged man looked at Tom and just shrugged, turning slowly toward the house without a word. Tom, Jimmy and Skeets stood still and silent, watching the family scene unfold. They were on the verge of getting back in their vehicles when the dowdy woman took a single step onto the porch and once again asserted herself.

"And you men get in here, too," she barked. "I'll not have men freezing to death on my front door. Get in here, I said. Now."

The three men turned and dutifully trudged up the three porch steps and into a small front room, still not saying a word. Tom removed his hat, and Jimmy pulled the knit cap from his oily hair. Skeets followed suit immediately, pulling off his camouflage hunting cap by one of its ridiculous orange felt earflaps. The young soldier and his wife had already disappeared deeper into the house, leaving the rest to fend for themselves.

A radio somewhere was playing the same steady catalogue of Christmas carols, and the house was warm with the smell of baking.

"I assume you are Mr. and Mrs. Willis," Tom finally said. "I'm Sergeant Tom Bennett, and these men are James Shuford and Randall Travers. They work for the county."

The couple simply nodded, with their usual deference to figures of authority.

"We found this young man out on 70 a little while back, and he told us he was headed here to be home with his family for Christmas, so we thought we might as well do what we could to help him get here and out of this weather as fast as we could. I'm sorry we made such a fuss, and I apologize if we caused you any concern. But we got him here safe and sound and in time for Christmas, and that seems to me to be what counts most."

The middle-aged man finally spoke. "You don't have to apologize for anything, Sergeant," he said. "Bobby called us from Fayetteville before he set out, so we knew he'd get here sometime, even in this weather. Can't say I expected him this soon. But I'm sure glad he got here in time for Christmas."

He paused. "He's a very determined young man," he went on. "We're proud to have him as our baby girl's husband. And we're grateful to you more than you know for getting him here tonight."

The woman spoke up when it became clear her husband was through talking.

"Yes, we're proud of him," she said. "If you men are family men, you know what having your loved ones around you means, especially on Christmas. So I want you to know I'm proud of you, too, for helping make that happen."

She paused, and her tone changed completely.

"Now you men take off those coats and give me your hats, and you sit down here in the kitchen with me for a few minutes. I'm baking bread tonight, and it's toasty warm. I always bake bread on Christmas. I'm going to fix you all some good hot coffee to take the chill out of your bones. I can fix hot chocolate if you like that better. But I am going to fix you something. No man goes away from my house on this or any other night cold or hungry or thirsty. Especially not after what you men have done for us. I just won't have it..."

Her husband interrupted her.

"Now, Jo Anne, you just calm down and do what you want to do," he said. "No one here is going to say no to a cup of coffee or a bite to eat. None of these gentlemen would be so rude as to do something like that. Not on this night, especially."

He paused. "Am I not right, gentlemen?"

Tom and Jimmy just nodded their agreement. Both were dumb-struck when Skeets was the one who chose to speak up.

"Ma'am, you say you got hot chocolate?" he said. "I sure do love hot chocolate."

The woman beamed.

"Then you sit right down and I'll fix you the best hot chocolate you've ever had," she purred, turning immediately to the cupboard be-hind her. The room grew quiet, except for the periodic rattle of pots and pans and cups and dishes of one sort or another, and the steady flow of Christmas carols from the unseen radio. Tom's thoughts began to wander.

He didn't know this man or woman, at least not personally. But he knew them nonetheless. A working man, probably late forties or early fifties. Blue polyester work pants above black ankle-high boots common to the factory and mill work floors that populated the busi-ness world hereabouts. A checked flannel shirt. A quiet man. A de-liberate man.

The woman was the same age, roughly, with mostly dark brown hair pulled back in a bun. Wearing a patterned dress, down to mid-calf, and an apron. Not a show apron, but a work apron, with more than a few noticeable stains and a distinct coating of flour all over. She baked, all right.

These were solid people, reliable people. They worked hard every day at essential but unexciting jobs. They kept modest but orderly homes, and they raised kids with simple values firmly entrenched. They went to church every Sunday and could be relied on to help others when needed.

Tom knew them, all right. They led lives very different from those of the well-educated and the white-collared and the affluent who pop-ulated Charlotte and Winston and points beyond. Theirs was a very different world, indeed -- a distinct and unique plane of existence in the rural south, in which they were merely ghostly figures in a spectral realm, mundane spirits moving unseen among the sophisticated and well-to-do, who knew better than to believe in ghosts. They were the invisible people, not because they lacked flesh and blood or served no practical or useful purpose, but rather because much of the rest of society simply chose not to see them.

They had been sitting comfortably for several minutes, with a steady stream of coffee and hot chocolate and cookies fueling a pleasant back-and-forth that engaged all of them – even Skeets. They were laughing when the young solider appeared in the kitchen door, holding something small in his arms, his wife standing just behind him, smiling beatifically. The conversation instantly went quiet when they saw them.

"Gentlemen, let me introduce you to Robert Ellison Simmons, Jr.," the young soldier said with no attempt to hide his pride.

The young soldier pulled back a pale blue blanket, revealing the tiny pink boy beneath. He's so small, so fragile, Tom thought. The baby had all the expected parts and wrinkles, plus a healthy head of fine dark hair. But his most compelling features undoubtedly were the clear, bright blue eyes. Newborn babies mostly have eyes that don't seem to focus on anything, Tom recalled. This one seems to look right into you.

The baby made not a sound and simply stared tranquilly at the family scene before him. At length he began to squirm – just a little, barely enough to notice. He slowly extended his small left arm, as if to show off his tiny clenched hand. The individual perfectly formed fingers of the hand slowly opened, ever wider, until the baby's forefinger made contact with one of the comparatively massive fingers on Tom's own outstretched hand. The touch lasted only a moment before the pure white hand slowly began to draw back into its original position. Tom wasn't sure if the gesture was meant to acknowledge those in attendance, or to bestow the child's own special blessing on one of those who had come so far to see him.

The three men took turns touching the baby's cheeks and stroking his fine hair, but none of them had much of anything to say. They were content just to look and smile and maybe reflect, each lost in his own thoughts. We must make quite a sight, Tom thought, three grown men fawning over a newborn babe like this, thinking about just how exceptional each new life could be, but too dumb and confused and inarticulate to know what to say about it.

He finally decided it was time to signal an end to this particular ceremony.

"Men, I don't know about you, but I've got to get back to work," he said. "The people of North Carolina are paying me good money to keep them safe on the roadways, holiday or not. It's almost midnight, if you haven't noticed, and these people have to get some rest. And this boy needs to learn right now there's no way Santa Claus is going to show up if he isn't asleep in his bed."

The three men turned toward the door.

"I wish you men would stay just a little while more," Mrs. Willis said as her husband began gathering their coats and hats from the back bedroom. "This is no night to be out and about, and I don't think the good people of North Carolina would begrudge you some time to mark something holy, like this night should be to all of us."

"Thank you, ma'am, but we have to get back to it," Tom said. "You folks need some private time, some time just for family. Not a bunch of strangers sitting in your kitchen."

Mrs. Willis twitched, as if she had just remembered something, then turned and scurried toward the kitchen. Mr. Willis simply shrugged in response to the collective look of puzzlement on the men's faces. He stepped toward them, handing over their coats and hats as he spoke quietly.

"You might have been strangers a couple of hours ago," he said. "After what you've done for us this evening, you're not strangers anymore. We're all family tonight, and from here on out, too. I want you to remember that."

The three men started pulling on their coats and tried to smile as they began shuffling toward the door. Tom had his hand on the handle when Mrs. Willis scurried back into the front room, three checked towels covering something in her arms.

"I told you this was the night I bake bread," she gushed. "You men are each going to take a loaf with you. You can take it home with you. Or you can eat it while its fresh and hot. On a night like this, I know what I would do if I was you. Besides, you can always come back for more any time you like."

Tom and Jimmy made the obligatory sounds of polite refusal, knowing full well the futility of the gesture. Skeets made no such pretense of politeness. He reached out for one of the loaves immediately, a huge grin spreading across his face beneath that stupid hunter's hat.

"Thank you, ma'am," he blurted out. "And merry Christmas to you."

"And merry Christmas to you, too, Randall," Mrs. Willis responded. Her eyes seemed to lose focus for a moment, and she stared a bit vacantly into space, lost in the moment.

"You know, every time somebody wishes somebody else a merry Christmas, that's really just another way of saying I love you," she said to no one in particular. She paused slightly and went on, only now looking each man in the eye one by one. "Well, isn't it? Isn't Christmas the time we're supposed to remember just how much we love one another?" She didn't wait for a response, and with a smile and a nod of her head turned cheerily in the direction of the kitchen and the omnipresent Christmas carols.

After she left the room, no one spoke for a short while. None of the men seemed to know quite what to say. At last, Tom remembered what had been nagging at him somewhere deep down ever since they arrived, and used that to break the awkward silence.

"We got to be on our way, men. But I still have Bobby's ditty bag in the cruiser," he said abruptly. "We can't forget that."

Jimmy spoke up immediately.

"I'll get it, Tom," he said. "I'm already suited up and you're not."

He turned quickly to Skeets.

"Skeets, give me a hand, will ya?"

Skeets never questioned anything Jimmy told him, and Christmas eve was no time to start. He followed him without hesitation. He nodded energetically at Mr. Willis as he followed Jimmy out the door and into the white wall of snow that still threatened to swallow the house.

Tom was still fumbling with the last button on his coat when Mr. Willis moved close to him, speaking very softly.

"Sergeant, thank you," he said. "I mean that. I know exactly what you've done for us here tonight, and I thank you."

Tom didn't know what to say, except "you're very welcome." Then out of nowhere, he heard himself add words he hadn't spoken in years. "And a blessed Christmas to you and your family."

"And to yours," Mr. Willis said solemnly.

The two men nodded quietly, and that was that.

Where are Johnny and Skeets, Tom thought as he headed out into the storm. They should have been back by now. He found the two standing at the open back door of the cruiser. The young soldier's ditty bag was on the seat in front of them, unzipped about halfway. Skeets was standing by Jimmy, holding what looked for the world like two wallets.

Maybe it was the many long years of law enforcement, but Tom's first thought was of robbery. They can't be stealing from that bag, he said to himself. As he drew closer he could see through the snow that Jimmy was stuffing something *into* the bag, and it sure looked like a wad of bills.

They were so focused on what they were doing they never heard Tom approaching.

"What are you two doing now?"

"Damn, Tom," Jimmy blurted, "you nearly scared the life out of me."

"I said, what are you doing?" Tom repeated, before his tone changed noticeably. "Are you doing what I think you're doing?"

"Tom, it's Christmas," Jimmy said slowly, amid the pervasive howl of the wind. "Those kids don't have squat. What kind of Christmas are they going to be able to give that baby boy?"

"They have plenty to give other than what money can buy," Tom responded.

"No doubt," Jimmy said. "But a few new warm clothes and some more food and maybe a couple more shiny toys won't hurt them any, or make them any less holy. And what am I gonna do with a few measly bucks that's more important than a dad's first Christmas with his son?"

Tom thought about it for a minute, still staring at Jimmy and Skeets.

"So how much did you put in?" he finally asked with an audible sigh, reaching for his own wallet.

"All I had on me," Jimmy answered. "About 60 bucks, I figure."

"I had 35," Skeets chimed in.

Tom sighed again. "Here's 55 more," he said, handing the bills to Jimmy. "I'm all in. You guys happy now?"

Jimmy didn't say anything to Tom.

"Skeets, you take this bag to Mr. Willis, pronto," he instructed. "Then get back into your truck double-quick. We got a lot of interstate to cover."

Jimmy strode toward his truck without another word. He was halfway into the cab when he seemed to pause. He turned his head toward his shoulder, not far enough to make eye contact, but spoke loudly enough to make sure he could be heard over the storm.

"Tom?" he said.

"Yeah, Jimmy?"

"Merry Christmas."

"Merry Christmas, Jimmy."

By now Skeets had sprinted back to his truck as best he could, and the three revved up their vehicles and labored noisily down the driveway back to the road. In no more than a minute, each was lost to sight amid the storm that raged unabated around them.

It took Tom almost an hour to get back to the At Your Service. It gave him plenty of time to check in with dispatch and confirm there were no reports of anything needing his attention, and to reflect privately and honestly on the night's events.

As expected, Darryl was still standing behind the counter, drinking a cup of coffee and reading a six-month-old copy of the National Enquirer.

"You get that soldier boy home?" he asked nonchalantly as Tom walked in.

"Yes, we did." That's all he had to say.

"Don't surprise me none in the least," Darryl said under his breath, without looking up from his reading.

The radio droned on with more Christmas carols as Tom fished through his wallet for the scrap of paper he kept there with important phone numbers on it. When he finally found it, he started looking for change in his pocket and was peeved to find he only had a quarter, a nickel and two dull pennies.

"Darryl," he called out. "You got some change? I need to make a call."

"You can't call through dispatch?" Darryl was puzzled.

"No, this is personal, and I'm a little short tonight," Tom said.

"How much you need?"

"I'm not sure. A buck or two at most."

Darryl sighed and closed the tabloid. He ambled over to the ancient cash register on the end of the counter and hit the No Sale button. "Take whatever you need," he said, leaving the drawer wide open as he walked toward his back room.

Tom took a handful of nickels, dimes and quarters, and laid them out in neat rows on the small shelf under the decrepit old pay phone on the station's wall. He wondered what kind of attitude he would have to endure from an operator who had to work on Christmas eve. He was surprised when she turned out to be both pleasant and helpful when he told her what he wanted to do and gave her the number scribbled on the scrap of paper from his wallet.

"That will be 85 cents of the first three minutes," she said. "Each extra minute will be 15 cents. You can pay as you go, or deposit as much as you like before we dial. But if you don't use all the time you pay for, you don't get anything back. I can't make refunds. I'd just pay as you go."

Tom thanked her and plunked four quarters into the slot. He kept four more grasped in his left hand, at the ready.

"You want me to dial now?" the operator asked.

"You bet," Tom said.

"I'll be glad to," she responded. "And sir, you have a merry Christmas."

"I plan on doing just that," Tom said. "And I hope you do, too."

The phone rang four times before Alex picked up. His voice was sleepy.

"Hello?"

"Alex, it's your dad," Tom said. "I know it's late and I'm sorry I woke you up."

Alex didn't respond at first.

"Dad, is that really you? What time is it?"

"It's almost two," Tom said.

"Two a.m.?" Alex seemed to need a little time to take it in. But in a flash, it became crystal clear he was finally awake. "Is something wrong? Is Mom okay?"

"Your mom is just fine, and so am I," Tom said in his best reassuring voice. "I just wanted to take a second to check on you, what with this storm and all. I apologize for calling you so late. But I was thinking about you a lot tonight, wondering if you're okay in this storm, and it being Christmas eve and all, I just...."

"Dad, that's okay," Alex cut in. "It's all right. I'm indoors and fine. Haven't been outdoors all day. But are you sure you're okay, though?"

"I'm fine, I'm fine," Tom said again. "I'm on duty tonight, and this has been the first chance I've had to talk, that's all."

He paused, trying to read Alex. He didn't wait long, though, before getting to what he really wanted to talk about.

"Listen, Alex, I've been thinking," he said. "We don't see you anywhere near as much as we should, or as much as I'd like. I don't want us to miss another Christmas if we can help it."

He paused again.

"So I was thinking, maybe your Mom and I drive down once this storm is over and we get to see you and this wonderful place you call Chapel Hill. We might even buy you a good meal or two while we're there. Just hang out. Catch up. You know."

He waited for some response, some indication of hope. He felt a wave of relief washed over him when he got exactly that from Alex.

"Sounds good to me," his son said. "Classes don't start until the second Monday after New Year's, so we got plenty of time. Come whenever you like and stay as long as you like. You're always welcome wherever I am. You know that. You've always known that."

Tom let the small rebuke pass without comment.

"Good," he said. "Consider it booked. I'll talk to your Mom and we'll pin down a date and start making some plans. I have leave to burn, so we can take whatever time we want."

"I'll wait to hear from one of you," Alex said. "But you better know in advance this place is very small and more than a little noisy from time to time. If you don't mind that, I won't either."

"Not a problem, son," Tom said. "Look, I got to get back on the road. You get back to sleep. We'll talk."

"Okay. Good night, Dad. Thanks for calling. And you and mom have a merry Christmas."

"Alex, it's Christmas, and Christmas should be all about family," Tom said. "Now you get some sleep. Good night, son. And merry Christmas to you, too… a very merry Christmas to all of us."

After he hung up, Tom walked to the station's door and just stared into the unrelenting snowstorm for several minutes before turning back to the pay phone. He dropped in a dime for the local call and dialed. It took a while for Ellie to pick up.

"Ellie, it's me," he said.

"Tom?" she said, instantly awake. "What is it, Tom? Are you okay?"

"I'm fine, I'm fine," he said calmly. "I'm sorry to wake you up in the middle of the night like this. But I thought you ought to know something I've done. It involves you just as much as me."

"What on earth are you talking about?" she said. "What could be so important you have to call me now, on Christmas eve?"

"Well, it's about Alex," he said.

She was immediately on edge. "Oh my God, something has happened to my baby boy."

"No, no, no," Tom interrupted. "He's fine. I just talked to him. I called him to ask if we could come down to Chapel Hill and spend some time with him before the holidays are over."

"Tom, you're not joking with me, are you? Cause if you are, it's not funny. It's not the least bit funny."

"No, I'm not joking. I'm very serious. This nonsense between us has to stop sometime, and I can't think of a better time to get started than Christmas eve."

Ellie didn't say anything for a moment. "Are you serious about this?" she finally asked.

"Yes, I am serious," Tom said with a sigh. "I mean it. And I want you to help put our family back together the way it's supposed to be. When I get home tonight, I want to sit down and start planning this trip out. I want to do it right."

It was quiet once again on the line. Tom chose to wait her out this time, and this time she broke the silence.

"Okay, if you really mean this, you know I'll do anything to make that happen. Oh, Tom, please tell me you really mean it."

"Hey, I already made the call, didn't I? We're committed. At least we are if you're ready to go along with the promises I've already made on behalf of both of us."

"I am," she responded. "You come on home and we'll talk more about this. I need some time to take all this in."

"I'll see you about six," he said. "Now you go back to bed and get some sleep." He paused.

"Merry Christmas, Ellie."

"Merry Christmas, Tom. You be careful."

Tom buttoned his coat and put on his hat, and started out to his cruiser. He was halfway out the door when he turned on his heel and marched back to the doorway to Darryl's little room. The old man was lying on his cot, staring blankly at the ceiling, apparently still listening to the Christmas carols coming from the ancient radio hanging precariously from a rickety shelf nailed to the wall.

"Merry Christmas, Darryl," he said.

"Why, merry Christmas to you, too, Tom."

Darryl sat up and watched Tom turn and walk out the door and drive off. He wasn't all that surprised how quickly the storm seemed to swallow up the big cruiser. What did nag at him, though, was why Tom would go out of his way to offer up a merry Christmas to him, of all people.

Normally Tom wasn't all that gushy or sentimental, Darryl reflected silently. But he'd been acting stranger and stranger as the night went on. Anybody could see that. But then and again, it is Christmas eve. God only knows what will go wandering through a man's mind on a night like this.

Break Thou the Bread of Life

Jesus said unto them, I am the bread of life — John 6:35 KJV

1. Break Thou the bread of life, Dear Lord, to me,
2. Bless Thou the truth, dear Lord, To me, to me,
3. Thou art the bread of life, O Lord, to me,
4. O send Thy Spir - it, Lord, Now un - to me,

As Thou didst break the loaves Be - side the sea;
As Thou didst bless the bread By Gal - i - lee;
Thy ho - ly Word the truth That sav - eth me;
That He may touch mine eyes, And make me see:

Be - yond the sa - cred page I seek Thee, Lord;
Then shall all bond - age cease, All fet - ters fall;
Give me to eat and live With Thee a - bove;
Show me the truth con - cealed With - in Thy Word,

My spir - it pants for Thee, O liv - ing Word.
And I shall find my peace, My all in all.
Teach me to love Thy truth, For Thou art love.
And in Thy Book re - vealed I see Thee, Lord.

WORDS: St. 1,2, Mary A. Lathbury, 1841-1913; st. 3,4, Alexander Groves, 1842-1909
MUSIC: William F. Sherwin, 1826-1888

BREAD OF LIFE
6.4.6.4.D.

This tune in a higher key, No. 368.

FISH STICKS & BALONEY

The many faces of a mother's love

CHALMERS RECAPTURED AT EAGLE MOTEL
AFTER WALKING AWAY FROM WORK CREW

MORGANTON, N.C., June 26 – Burke County Police deputies took escaped convict Randall Chalmers into custody without incident last night at the Eagle Motel on Carbon City Road, following a tip to the CrimeStoppers Hotline by an anonymous female caller.

Chalmers, 23, yesterday morning walked away from a roadside refuse-collection crew from the Roberts Correctional Camp (RCC), where he had served four months of a seven-month sentence for public intoxication and destruction of public property.

Deputy Frank Whisnant said Chalmers surrendered voluntarily at 11:25 p.m. in room 21 at the motel, where he was surrounded by empty Domino's pizza boxes and the remnants of a 12-pack of Old Milwaukee beer. "Actually, he seemed pretty happy and was quite pleasant about the whole thing," Whisnant said.

RCC spokeswoman Roberta Shoup said Chalmers would face an administrative hearing to determine the nature and extent of any penalty for his escape, for review by the Burke County Superior Court. She declined to speculate on what penalty might result.

"Randy has been a model inmate up till now," she said. RCC staff members speaking anonymously said Chalmers had grown increasing critical of the variety, volume and quality of food served to inmates but had given no indication his dissatisfaction was strong enough to make him a sufficient flight risk to preclude service on the road crew.

Shoup said Chalmers simply walked unseen into the woods near Exit 107 of Interstate 40 sometime between 10:45 a.m. and noon. An investigation into the incident has been initiated at RCC, which will include a review of existing surveillance procedures for the voluntary work crews that perform highway clean-up services.

"Normally these crews are made up of inmates who have earned a degree of trust," Shoup said. "This kind of thing hardly ever happens, but we'll look into it to see how we can make sure it doesn't occur again."

Whisnant said police have no indication of how Chalmers traveled from the Exit 107 area to the motel, located approximately six miles west of the spot where he disappeared.

Motel Manager Charley Settlemyre said the room was rented in mid-afternoon by "a kinda fat, middle-aged woman," who registered as "Mrs. Alma Probst" and paid $39.70 for the room in cash. All the registration information subsequently proved to be fictitious, he said. Settlemyre added that he saw no sign of Chalmers at any time and felt no need to verify the identity of the person renting the room, or the information provided about address and vehicle.

"We get a lot of rentals like that, so I didn't think anything about it," Settlemyre said. "Most of 'em are a lot younger than her, though."

Domino's Manager Clyde Adderly said records show a 7:05 p.m. phone-in order for delivery to room 21 at the Eagle Motel. Domino's driver Stevie Cooke said a young man cheerfully accepted delivery of the food at 7:40 p.m. and paid the $16.75 bill in cash.

"Yeah, I remember real good," Cooke said. "Was a large supreme meat lover's pizza and cinnamon sticks. Handed me a twenty and told me to keep the change. Gave me a cold one, too. Seemed like a cool guy."

Chalmers' mother, Mrs. Claudine Chalmers of Mt. Olive Road, said she regretted the escape but was relieved the whole matter was over peacefully.

"He's a real good boy, my Randy," she said. "He just got so tired of fish sticks and baloney, he had to have something good to eat." Mrs. Chalmers denied any knowledge of her son's intent to escape or his reasons for taking a room at the Eagle Motel, or who may have booked the room or reported his location to the CrimeStoppers Hotline.

Shoup disputed suggestions that the RCC food program bore any responsibility for Chalmers' actions. "We may not offer steak and lobster, but we do pretty good on a food budget of $2.90 a day for each inmate," she said.

Whisnant said Chalmers would be transferred from the Burke County Detention Center to RCC sometime today.

"I hope it all works out for him," he said. "He didn't seem such a bad sort. He even offered me and T.J. (fellow Burke Deputy T.J. Stickle) his last two cans of Old Milwaukee."

Whisnant said he and Stickle declined the offer.

"We said no, but I admit we thought about it for a minute," he said. "After all, the city and county commissioners haven't seen fit to give the police a raise in over four years, so none of us can afford to buy a whole lot of beer or anything else anymore."

Count Your Blessings

Johnson Oatman

Edwin O. Excell

BOOBS OUT

A modern guide for the married man

Most people react much the same way when I tell them I've been married for over 35 years.

"Really?"

"You gotta be kidding!"

"No way."

"Good God Almighty."

In other words, incredulity. Then the inevitable follow-up:

"How do you do it?"

"What's your secret?"

"Good God Almighty."

For years and years, I assumed this sense of amazement was a telling commentary on the sad state of the institution of marriage these days. Half of all marriages today end in divorce, you know.

But over time, perhaps in progression with the steady loss of self-esteem that has accompanied my advancing years, I began to realize something else – something far more personal – was behind these universal expressions of amazement, wonder and doubt. It finally dawned on me that their incredulity stemmed more from their opinion of me than from our apparent triumph over the pervasive divisive forces ravaging one of our most fundamental social structures.

What they were really asking was far simpler: How can anyone stay married to someone like you – for any length of time, let alone more than three decades?

I admit, I'm not really much of a prize. I'm a little slow on the uptake, and my social graces and interpersonal skills have been described with the same word – "lacking." My high school guidance counselor once advised me to consider pursuing a career as a hermit. Well into my sixties, I'm still delighted with the variety of sounds my body can make, especially in elevators, some almost on command. I have a bit of a temper, and I'm forgetful of minor things like names, addresses, phone numbers, computer log-in names and passwords, gambling debts, household chores, due-dates, rules of grammar and such foo-fah.

But I never, ever forget our anniversary, and maybe that's the real secret behind our marital longevity.

Every year, I make it a point to give my wife a card, some flowers and some form of gift, however token in nature. Long ago I learned the futility of anything that couldn't be returned or exchanged with minimal effort. Each gift had to be "nice" – not necessarily anything that would fall into the category of "capital asset," but something beyond perfume or a sweater, and as I learned very early on, nothing as purely practical as a case of motor oil or super-economy-size package of vacuum cleaner bags. But it was the gesture, the effort, the act of remembrance, that counted most.

To enrich the commemoration, I also have consistently added my own special fillip to the gift-giving. Each year, especially after we got past the big 40th birthday milestone, I've made it a point to always add something truly intimate, and every now and then something outright naughty, to the package. A pair of lacy underwear, a sexy teddy, once even a bottle of sparkly body glitter.

I don't trumpet it from the rooftops, but I love my wife, still. I love her despite the occasional spats she always causes, the dented fenders that appear on her car regular as clockwork, the crazy relatives who show up unannounced to cry or borrow money, the never-ending conspiracy to hide the TV remote, the refrigerator space wasted on vegetables, and all that. And I love her despite the added pounds, the extra wrinkles, the bit of sag here and there.

I like to tell her that no matter how many years we mark with birthdays, anniversaries or other milestones of life, I remain both in love and in lust with her, and she actually smiles when I say it. And God help me, to this day, when I look at her sometimes, I still see her standing there in the wedding dress she wore so well on that sunny, warm June afternoon so many years ago.

So every year I make sure to add that little something extra – that naughty little nothing that says I don't just *love* you, I still *want* you. Not one has ever been actually worn, mind you. In fact, I can't tell you where they all have gone, or to what purpose they have been put, or by whom. I just know they've never actually been on her person, at least in my presence, and never will be. Truth is, she never needs to, to keep me interested and coming home night after night. It's the thought, and the little extra effort behind it, not the physical reality, that's important. That's the secret.

It's not always easy, either. I'm the typical male, and shopping is not my forte, especially shopping for someone of the opposite sex. It's double or triple difficult when it involves – *ahem* – intimate apparel.

It goes far beyond simple momentary embarrassment for me, and I suspect all males other than Sean Connery or Brad Pitt or Gerard Butler or their modern ilk. It's humiliating, to be blunt, and it's a major cause of diminished testosterone levels, I'm certain. The internet and on-line shopping offer no better option or promise of invisibility, at least to me. The last thing I need is to wind up on a few hundred of *those* mailing lists, as my one-time on-line purchase of some vitamins proved certain. But love conquers all, and year after year I summon the resolve to conquer my aversion to humiliation and hormonal imbalance, and I trek out on the hunt for just the right thing.

Over the years, some of the less painful forays evolved into kind of a pattern. A few select, preferred shops became my go-to sources. Small, out-of-the-way shops, far across town, with poor lighting, inside and out, and staff that always appeared to be mostly stoned and completely indifferent to the seedy looking old coot who showed up every year just before June, and to most other customers, I suspect.

And yes, for those of my loyal readers with vivid, active and slightly prurient imaginations, sometimes that old coot was wearing a raincoat, but that's because it was raining. It was, I swear.

Routine and familiarity never completely eliminated the embarrassment, but it made it quick, and that helped make it more bearable. At least, until the year I was out of town on an extended work assignment and had to take my quest for a token of my unquenched amorous fire into strange and alien territory... *truly* strange and alien territory: Detroit.

I was there for several weeks, actually, on a contract assignment, and my timing was off that year. It dawned on me one night after a long, long day at the grindstone that the clock was ticking, faster than I had realized. I'd be home for the anniversary, all right, but time for shopping would be non-existent. I already had a nice ring in hand from an earlier trip into New York – a real gift, one she would appraise and deem acceptable, I was sure. But I would have absolutely no time to fulfill the shopping quest for the token-of-lusty-affection component of the package when I returned home. I had to take care of it here and now, like it or not.

So instead of heading straight back to my room-by-the-week accommodations that night, I set out on a mission to find *the* gift. I drove through suburb after suburb, blindly seeking just the right kind of place. Not one of the major department stores, where cameras might lurk unseen. A small place, off the beaten track, with little foot traffic. Not a sex shop, exactly, but pretty darn close to it.

And I found it.

It was called The Love Connection. It was a small shop in a strip mall reeking of the 1960s, located in a nondescript neighborhood. It was in an out-of-the-way location near the end of the strip, away from the parking lot entrance and well out of sight. It had poor lighting, even in the tiny display window showing a one-armed mannequin wearing a sheer white nightie. A scuba tank repair shop occupied the space next door, and a restaurant uniform supply store sat next to that. It was perfect.

It was almost 9 p.m. when I strode in manfully, confident this would be easy and quick. Grab something and go, I told myself. No one knows you. No one will recognize you. No one cares. Walk quickly. Don't make conversation, or even eye contact, unless you absolutely have to. Now think of Michael Jordan and just *do* it.

It took a second for my eyes to adjust once I entered the establishment. Instead of the cramped, dark and seedy interior I had expected, I found a brightly lit room extending far, far into the distance, filled with rack after rack of ladies intimate apparel, evenly mixed among what I would call the sexy, the naughty, the profane and the painful. It was a pervert's paradise.

I stood momentarily blinded and transfixed, like the proverbial deer in the headlights, for God knows how long. The out of nowhere, I heard a voice, apparently directed at me.

"Hep you?"

Standing before me was a young African-American woman, maybe 30 years old, not quite five feet tall but still fully believable as a back-up middle linebacker for the Lions. I stared blankly.

"Sir, can I do something for you?" She forced me to make eye contact.

"Uh, yeah," I blurted back. "Yes, ma'am, you can. I need an anniversary gift for my wife."

"What you got in mind?" she replied.

"Oh, I don't know. Something sexy."

She struggled to maintain her professionalism.

"You mean like a nightie?" she said. I just stared blankly.

She continued. "Maybe some harem pants? A corset? Crotchless panties?"

I stared some more.

"I don't know," I finally croaked. "Why don't you pick something out for me?"

She was growing frustrated, I could tell.

"Well, tell me what she likes, and what she is like," she said.

"She likes flannel pajamas," I managed to respond. "And she loves to read, and she is great with kids and animals."

The clerk was now fully vexed.

"No, sir. I mean, what does she *look* like? Is she tall or short? How much does she weigh? What does she like to wear for your romance time?"

I struggled to take it all in.

"Oh, I see what you mean," I said. "Well, she likes nighties."

"And what do you like?"

God's honest truth, I first thought she was asking me what I liked to wear on romantic nights, and I had a mental flash of myself in the men's sequined silver thong I could see suspended between two hooks on the wall behind the clerk, next to the leather riding crop. Then I figured out her real meaning. But I can't explain what I blurted out next.

"Maybe a corset." It was more of a question than a statement, but it was enough.

"What size?" she shot back.

I just mumbled. How the hell was I supposed to know something like that? Corsets have *sizes*?

"What size dress does she wear?"

I stared some more.

"Well, describe her. How tall is she?"

About five one. I was sure of that.

"How much does she weigh?"

Now, in any other situation, I knew the correct answer would be "108, maybe 110." But I also knew that was off by an order of magnitude that never dared be spoken, ever, to anyone. So I mumbled some more.

"Is she as heavy as me?"

No one is as heavy as you, I thought.

"Maybe a little smaller," I said diplomatically.

"Is she round or curvy?"

Curvy, I said. Definitely curvy.

"How big is her butt?"

"About like mine, I suppose."

Another not-so-little white lie. But it was the best I could do, even though it clearly didn't seem to appease the clerk.

"How big is her chest?"

By what standard or method of comparison, I asked myself, as I mumbled yet more unintelligible gibberish.

"Is her bosom like mine? Smaller, or bigger?"

That one I knew. "Bigger," I said, with pride.

"How much bigger?"

We're back to that comparative thing again, I thought.

"A lot bigger," I said confidently.

"You mean like grapefruit?" she asked.

"More like honeydew melons," I replied.

Well, maybe I exaggerated *just* a little, but she *is* a tad busty. And besides, that was nowhere near as big a departure from the truth as the much more frequently made assertion that she weighed 110 pounds.

"Lordy, she gonna need a boobs-out, then," the clerk said as she turned on her heel and strode toward the back of the shop.

She called out to a co-worker as she walked. Not a quiet, conversational call, mind you. A full-throated, from-the-diaphragm, all-points-bulletin, Southern-Baptist-choir bellow, effective for interplanetary as well as intra-shop communication.

"Wendy, where are those Fandango boobs-out we got in last week? This man wants to take a look at 'em."

Wendy called out from an unseen location in response. "The crotchless ones, or the snap-crotch ones?"

Heads began to pop up one by one from between the racks all through the store. All men. All middle-aged or older. All wearing rain coats. And like the few women customers sprinkled throughout the shop, suddenly very curious, either with the nature of these Fandango creations, or the new-guy pervert interested in them.

"Don't matter," my clerk called back. "He don't know which one he wants. Not till he sees them, is my bet."

"Rack 21," Wendy responded. I looked to my left and saw a sign saying "Rack 4." It was going to be a long walk. A very long walk, like hiking across Texas. They always are when so many eyes are upon you.

"My name is Glorianna," my clerk said, trying to cement the sales relationship as she led me toward the back of the store. "What's yours?"

"George Clooney," I said.

"Like the actor?" Glorianna's face lit up as she asked.

"Just like the actor," I replied.

I never liked George Clooney. Damn good actor, but way too smug and full of himself. If somebody was going to be embarrassed, it should be him, not me. A mental picture flashed through my mind, of a National Enquirer cover: "Clooney nabbed in Motor City perv sweep."

In short order, Glorianna had two of the reddest, gaudiest things I've ever seen laid out in front of me. They looked like corsets, as best I understand the concept of corset-ness. But where I expected to see some kind of brassiere-like superstructure up top, there were only two wire semi-circles stitched into the fabric.

Ah, boobs _out_. I suddenly got it.

"Now, the crotchless is sure sexy," Glorianna was saying. "But the snap-crotch holds things in place better, if you get what I mean. Won't ride up so much. Lot more comfortable, especially when you start wiggling and bouncing around. And you can always unsnap it when the right time comes, can't ya? Laces up in the back, so one size is supposed to fit everybody. Well, I suppose it might fit 'most everybody. But I always say get the large, unless you're some kind of beanpole."

She sure knew how to sell the merchandise.

"I'll take the large snap-crotch," I said decisively. "Got any kind of gift box to put it in? Maybe some scented body oil?"

By now, decorum and discretion no longer mattered. Might as well go with it, I remember thinking at the time. Glorianna beamed with delight at the prospect of yet another satisfied customer. Or maybe she worked on commission.

"You're gonna like this, and so will she," Glorianna editorialized. "You know, you are a lucky man, to be able to do stuff like this for your lady. Romance should never die. I really like it when I see people who understand that. Yes sir, you must be blessed. Truly blessed."

I paid with cash – obviously – and strode out of the shop and drove into the night.

The following week, my wife oohed and ahhed over the ring, and spent exactly three seconds examining the corset. "Hmmm," was all she said. "A boobs-out." She tossed it on a pile of clothes next to her dresser, never to be seen again. Mission accomplished, I reflected silently.

But what lasted a lot longer in my mind as I watched the ritual play out was that one simple thing Glorianna had said. You must be blessed. Truly blessed.

Indeed I am. Not because I can please my wife with gifts, sexy or otherwise. Not because we've been able to accumulate a lot of things over the years, either capital assets or tawdry sentimentalities. Being blessed doesn't mean having the largest house in the fanciest subdivision, or a higher than average rate of return on your investment portfolio, or the lowest golf handicap at the country club. Blessings don't come exclusively as 35-foot sailboats or computer-controlled luxury sedans, or lake cabins and fine Bordeaux, or rings or even sexy underwear. They may not come from any of those 'things.'

What makes us both blessed is having something a lot more important than things. It's caring enough about each other to overlook the shortcomings and failures, and the idiosyncrasies and foibles, and the unintended yet inevitable slights and hurts that pile up over the years. It's each of us wanting to please the other, in matters large and small. It's finding pleasure in giving and sharing, not so much of things, but more so of each other. It's knowing each other's fears and worries and delights and dreams, and accepting them all, and being there to help deal with or pursue or escape each as best we can, together. We're blessed to have each other, warts and all, and to know just how special and powerful this love between us really is. That's the blessing, and its value is beyond rubies and gold.

I hope I can sustain that thought in the weeks ahead. It's getting close to June once again, and it's getting tougher and tougher to find that special little extra at our advancing age, and I've misplaced my rain coat to boot. But two thoughts comfort me.

One, I know my wife will smile and squeeze my hand, gently, as she always does, when she opens the annual anniversary package, no matter what is inside. It's the gesture, the thought, the celebration of the blessings we already share, that counts.

And two, I know how to get to Detroit.

Onward, Christians Soldiers

ONWARD,
CHRISTIAN SOLDIERS

The great beyond oddly beckons

In the draft-fueled Army of my youth, true happiness, if not outright survival, was based on a consummate skill in the art of being invisible, at all times and in all places. No matter how many people are present, no matter what the circumstance, just blend into the background. Never volunteer. Never be first in line. Never do anything so well – or so badly – as to attract attention, or to be noticed at all, for that matter.

So I have no one but myself to blame for winding up on the U.S. Army Intermountain Funeral Team, and the adventures that followed. I simply let my mind wander and accidentally made eye contact with the First Sergeant as he walked through the ranks during company formation that cold winter morning.

"West," he bellowed in his normal cheery 6 a.m. voice, just before releasing the assembled HQ Company. "Report to the XO immediately after company dismissal." He smiled a knowing and evil smile as he said it, I recall. This can't be anything good, I also remember thinking at the time. Oh, how right I was.

Lieutenant Bevins wore his usual look of puzzlement and mild despair when I reported to his cramped office as ordered. I often wondered why dealing with the enlisted men caused him so much obvious angst. After all, this was a Vietnam combat veteran – a brave young man who had led others into, and more important, out of battle. But he struggled with this sort of routine, mostly administrative interaction, and we all recognized it, and tried to take advantage of it as best we could.

"West, I can't find any record at all of you on any service detail," he said with genuine surprise as he shuffled through the company duty records in his hands.

"You've been part of this company for nine months and apparently haven't done one post or company duty in the whole time," he went on. "*Not one.* Is that right?"

"I can't recall having been assigned to one, sir," I said, standing in what passed for a state of attention. "Perhaps the Army thought my staff job was more important."

"You're a glorified file clerk in the camp personnel office," Lt. Bevins snorted as he stared at the papers some more.

"Well, you're being assigned to one now," he went on after a small pause, still shuffling the papers, as if re-reading them might somehow change their contents. "The funeral team has an opening. Prescovitz got the measles. You're the new firing squad team B leader."

I panicked, despite myself, but tried hard not to let it show. The funeral team was the worst possible duty anyone could draw – more like a punishment detail. It involved traveling huge distances across the intermountain west, from the Montana border in the north to the Arizona state line in the south, trapped in two ancient olive-drab stretch company limousines with 14 other grunts and assorted equipment, driving non-stop night and day to provide deceased veterans with an official U.S. Army send-off. Overnight accommodations weren't part of the deal, and as full-time Army ambassadors, all team members were required to remain in Class A uniforms – and in full possession of admittedly limited faculties and some passable semblance of sobriety, if not dignity, at all times. In other words, it meant extended periods of time trapped in a travelling fart factory, neat, clean and sober. To 20-something-year-old children of the flower-power generation far away from home and friends, it was consignment to hell on earth. It was referred to, with an even mix of solemnity and nihilistic despair, as "riding the green weenie."

All this terrible truth, and more, cascaded through my consciousness in a nano-second. Stay calm, I told myself. Think. Think fast. Maybe I could still reverse engineer some kind of invisibility and escape this impending calamity.

"Well?" Lt. Bevins said, as beads of fear-sweat began to break out on my forehead. My brain went into overload. Synapses failed to function. I had nothing.

Lt. Bevins ended the torture. "Report to Sergeant Esperanza at 1600. Dismissed." I saluted, with a somewhat limp and bloodless wrist, I admit. But I saluted.

Master Sergeant Alberto Esperanza was an Army lifer – and not a man to be trifled with. He'd seen and done it all in his 20-odd years in the Army and his two tours in Nam. He ran the funeral team the same way he approached every assignment ever handed to him – with absolute commitment to doing the job right, and with an iron fist to make sure others under his command did the same. In this case, there was something more in play. He believed the funeral team was more than just another duty, like KP. It was a solemn obligation. It was the Christian thing to do. The tiny silver crucifix we all knew he wore on the chain with his dog tags wasn't there for show.

Our job is to provide the last full measure of respect these men have earned through their service to this great country, he would say, again and again. And he meant it. And by the living God, sweet Jesus and the Virgin Mary, we'd better believe it, and live it every time we head out on a mission – or we would answer to him, and eventually them, too. But first him.

The funeral detail involved providing gravesite support at the actual interment. One squad – the grave detail – carried the deceased from the hearse to the grave, folded the U.S. flag that draped the coffin, and presented it to the family. A second squad – the rifle team – stood at a respectful distance from the grave and fired three crisp volleys over the grave as the flag was folded. A single bugler played Taps as the flag was presented. Then we all stood at attention for a few moments, as the NCO in charge read the crowd and decided the appropriate moment for us to march silently and respectfully away.

My job, it turned out, was to serve as a rifleman in the firing squad – and to stand by as the back-up firing squad commander, in case the regular commander got sick, ran away, was beamed up by aliens, or whatever. Luckily, I never had to feel the weight of command.

The funeral team assignment meant we were on call for any burial in our designated area. The call to go could come at any time, on any day. It was an add-on 'honor' duty, meaning you had to do your regular job as usual, on top of this special responsibility. 'Comp time' hadn't yet been invented.

It also required me to re-familiarize myself with the old M-14s used by the rifle team. As the weapon of funeral-team choice, the M-14 was held to be far superior to the M-16 in combat use at that time. It actually looked like a real rifle, with a rich wood finish we polished to a blinding sheen, rather than a cold, sterile synthetic stock. It sounded more like a real rifle, even when firing blank cartridges. It seemed to evoke a greater sense of the "old" military that so many of our clientele had experienced. The M-14 was heavy, and a bear to clean, but hey, it was a real *weapon,* rich in history and symbolism.

After a few practice sessions under Sgt. Esperanza's direction, and with the support of the other members of the rifle team, I got the hang of things. We actually weren't bad at cranking out three short, sharp and unified volleys. And over the next few months, we had ample opportunity to display that unique skill.

Riding the green weenie was all it had been cracked up to be, and more. There is no way to convey the sheer boredom and physical misery spawned by spending hour after hour in an un-air conditioned pre-Humvee capable of seating nine uncomfortably, or 12 if deemed appropriate by the CO, traversing the vast, featureless desert reaches of the great American West. There is no way to capture the spiritual ennui, or the steady devolution of intellectual capacity, that comes from endless hours of healthy intellectual debate among equals on the true nature of breast esthetics, or which super-heroes would be the most effective tag-team partners in a wrestling ladder match, or which figure from history could eat the most hot dogs (without throwing up). There is no way to measure the exact frequency or true extent of finger-pulling among a gaggle of enlisted Army personnel trapped in a confined space for long periods of time. Even so, in time we became sufficiently proficient and trustworthy that Sgt. Esperanza no longer felt obliged to accompany us on some assignments, delegating overall command to the grave detail NCO. After all, we were professional soldiers.

So onward we marched, in fulfillment of our mission, and in pursuit of answers to the questions that vexed us. Life became a study in the duality of existence – long periods of time in search of something – *anything* – to provide distraction from life's pedestrian curse, balanced against short periods of absolute focus, complete control and strict adherence to carefully prescribed ritual. Eventually, most of us settled into a simple yet satisfying routine, sending the deceased off with a flair and flourish, and filling in the travel time with vigorous intellectual give and take, and the occasional quiet time made transcendent by the obscenely gratifying fantasy of filling in our DD 214 – the paperwork through which our active service to our country ended. But nothing lasts forever, not even desultory routine.

Our own version of Waterloo came on a particularly hot summer day somewhere in southern Utah, so remote from civilization that its name has become lost in the mists of memory. It was an easy trip compared to most, maybe a five- or six-hour drive, and we were all fresh and on top of our game. Or so we thought.

Our task that fine day was to provide a standard service for a very, very aged veteran, whose service in fact dated back to World War I. The fine gentleman had rolled his wheel chair gently into that celebrated good night in his 90-something[th] year, as I recall, and his funeral had been attended by at least four generations of a particularly extended family. Indeed, his young widow (probably no more than 85) was now seated front and center at the grave for the final act in the sad ritual of passage, shielded from the blazing sun by a phalanx of black umbrellas, surrounded by receding semi-circles of family and friends – ancient and decrepit close in, with younger and heartier men and women radiating out behind her central seat.

I guess there were more than 100 people there that day, which was a lot more than usual, and certainly a very big event indeed in this part of the world. It was a house worthy of our best possible performance. They got a performance, all right.

Initially, there was absolutely no sign of anything wrong, or any reason to worry. The sun beat down steadily. A small breeze ever-so-slightly moved a few of the white handkerchiefs that dotted the John Ford-like landscape scene, as a quiet murmur moved through the crowd awaiting arrival of the hearse. At last it came, and slowly backed into position about 50 feet from the grave.

The grave detail moved quickly and quietly and respectfully into position. Six strong young men, resplendent in their impressive uniforms, one by one took hold of the casket rails and began the slow, deliberate march to the grave, led by the grave detail leader at the coffin's head. The firing squad already had quietly and invisibly moved into position, line abreast of the grave just another 50 feet away, and stood watchful and ready at present-arms.

No one afterward could say exactly *why* it happened. But everyone agreed on *what*.

As the casket approached the grave, the detail leader assumed his usual backward-step routine, to guide placement of the coffin on the open grave railing. But today, instead of neatly side-stepping the burial hardware, his right foot slipped under the brass railing around the grave, thrusting him off-balance.

Now, I'd like to say that the detail leader was sufficiently agile and alert enough to take appropriate counter-steps, and thus salvage honor and dignity for all involved. But I can't. He fell backward into the open grave. Not an awkward, somersault-style fall, mind you. His military training must have kicked in, at least at some subconscious level. Rather than tuck-and-roll, or flail for balance and support, he simply went rigid, as if at full attention, and fell like a cement statue, backward, into the open grave.

As if to add a special icing to this celebratory cake, the detail leader managed to add his own color commentary to his fall from grace. With a firm voice and simple air of resignation, he managed during the act of falling to utter a profanity known throughout military and civilian history alike for its vileness, crudity and yet puzzling applicability to almost any bad situation: "Ah, ----." It hung in the air like a noxious cloud for what seemed an eternity, and in fact probably is still echoing loudly as it continues to hurtle through time and space beyond our solar system.

The assembled multitude, in contrast, made not one sound. They simply stared in what I suppose was mute disbelief. I know for sure it was mute, anyway. It could have been shock or maybe horror or very possibly outrage rather than disbelief, though.

The detail leader, fortunately, had the courage and discipline to make what true optimists would say was the best of an admittedly very bad situation. In an instant, he sprang from the grave as if launched from a cannon, and without missing a beat resumed direction of the well-rehearsed process of folding the flag, followed by a stately walk to the widow's chair for presentation of the tightly wrapped banner of honor, and the requisite slow salute.

My rifle team, meanwhile, displayed considerably less savoir faire. Our job was to fire the three volleys during the folding and presentation process, on order of the detail leader, in his best resonant baritone command voice. Only today, his command voice was somewhere between tenor and alto, according to witnesses afterward, although I distinctly remember a much higher basic tonal quality, more like a gifted lyric coloratura in the lower end of the soprano register. Memory no doubt plays tricks, however, and the actual range is of little if any true significance.

For our particular contribution to the whole unfortunate event, a squeaky voice was only the appetizer in a veritable banquet of disaster. PFC Mossberg started it all, really, when he outright giggled at the jack-in-the-box performance unfolding before him. His mirth spread virulently through the entire squad, and although most of us controlled it somewhat better, it nonetheless left us spasmodically twitching as we struggled to control our own involuntary guffaws. When the first order to "fire" finally came (an F-sharp above middle C, I argue), we were hopelessly out of control. That volley – and each of the two that followed – resonated across the scene like a string of Chinese firecrackers, haphazard markers more appropriate to the lunar new year or a Three Stooges festival than anyone's last rites. The order to turn left face and march away couldn't come soon enough. I won't begin to try to describe what Taps sounded like that day.

We secured the weapons and hit the road in record time. Initially, all was quiet, with each man lost in his own thoughts on the day's events. No, actually, all of us were thinking the same thing: How are we going to explain this to Sgt. Esperanza? Never mind what the CO or XO will think or say. We know how to handle them. But Esperanza could very well kill all of us, or make us wish we were dead. Literally. Regardless, we're all going to hell after this.

After the first three hours of panic, however, things began to seem a bit more manageable. You had to admit, it was one helluva burial service. They won't forget that one anytime soon in southern Utah. They may even tell stories about it around campfires, or maybe somebody will write a song. The mood eventually changed once again as we drove along in the increasing darkness and monotony of the landscape, and we had time to think seriously about all that had transpired. What did that poor family think of all of this? Hadn't we let them down? Had we somehow diminished this man's life and his service? He was a veteran. He didn't do anything to earn this.

From out of nowhere, somebody produced a small tablet and a Bic pen, and the next thing anyone knew we began drafting letter of apology to the widow and family. It wasn't poetry, and probably not all that grammatically correct, either. But it was sincere. We were heartily sorry if in our attempts to provide some measure of appropriate reverence and dignity we had fallen short of the standards we aspire to uphold – professionalism and respect in our every action, dignity and esteem for those we honor, and compassion and consideration for those who remain. Please accept our sincere condolences. Please forgive any shortcomings. There was more, but that kind of sums up the real heart and soul of it.

It wasn't much, really. But one of the great memories I take from an otherwise unmemorable stint of Army service is the sincerity of those words – and the full and honest belief in them from every one of that team of very different, yet at that moment very alike, men.

We got back to post sometime before midnight that night, signed in and stowed the weapons and gear. Nobody said much, and for whatever reason I got the assignment of typing up the letter. Maybe it was because I had access to a typewriter and could get the widow's name and address from the company clerk, who owed me money related to a shared investment in a fine domestic canned beverage the previous weekend. Anyway, the entire team came by my barrack's room bay, one by one, the following day to sign it, and I posted it with a stamp I bought off the evening duty clerk at HQ Company. Charged me double the face value, too.

Sgt. Esperanza asked how everything had gone, as was his habit, and we all gave the same evasive answer. By the book, Sarge. By the book. Meanwhile, we hoped it would all just somehow go away, but nonetheless stood by with fatalistic resignation for someone from the family to drop the dime on us. While we waited in limbo, one of the team members from the motor pool actually looked up Leavenworth in the post guide in the camp library.

It was several weeks later before the letter arrived. It went directly to the company CO, too. But we all got to see it eventually. In a short page of the most precise handwriting I've ever seen, the widow thanked us for all we had done to honor her late husband. She went on and on about how he loved the military and had been happy to serve his country when the forces of evil had to be defeated… how he talked so much about all the trials and tribulations he and other soldiers had to overcome almost every day, to do their duty… and how proud he would have been with the way we handled a difficult situation and maintained our focus on our duties, and how clear our concern for her and the family had been. Her most sincere thanks, and best wishes for the lives we all were beginning so auspiciously, she concluded.

It was a classy thing to do, and it saved our bacon, no doubt. We all knew it, but no one said anything about it. The CO and XO were happy, so much so they actually posted the letter on the company bulletin board. It may be hanging there still, 30 years on, for all I know. Sgt. Esperanza knew there was more to the story. He was like that. He looked at all of us kind of funny for a while, but said nothing more about it. We just went on with the dull day-to-day of Army life, with an occasional foray into the funereal world from time to time.

And maybe it's my imagination, but I believe we got even better at it after that. We had a different attitude, I know that much. I know I paid more attention to the faces of the people at the services. I thought more about what they were feeling, and what the march toward the grave must be like, and how that changes everything, for everybody, eventually. The way we think about life. What's funny and not funny. What really matters, and what doesn't.

I also had a lot of time to reflect on that poor widow's letter, and why she chose to respond the way she did. I have often heard it said that with age comes wisdom, but I can't recall anyone saying anything about a link between advancing years and a willingness to forgive. Maybe wisdom and forgiveness are really just flip sides of the same coin. That fine old lady's willingness to forgive certainly made me a better person, and maybe just a little smarter one, too.

If all that is true, I sure hope whoever fills out my final earthly DD 214 will keep it in mind when Taps is sounded for me. But by then, the whole notion of a funeral team probably will have gone the way of the dodo, replaced by a squad of robotic riflemen firing in perfect unison, with gyroscopically balanced automaton pallbearers and a mechanized flag-folding device, accompanied by a digitized Taps played on micro-speakers, all controlled by a pasty-skinned nerd with two chevrons and a smartphone. If so, I for one will regret it.

But I also promise you this: I won't say a word.

This Is My Father's World

In the beginning God created the heavens and the earth — Genesis 1:1 NIV

1. This is my Fa - ther's world, And to my lis - t'ning ears, All
2. This is my Fa - ther's world, The birds their car - ols raise; The
3. This is my Fa - ther's world, O let me ne'er for - get That

na - ture sings, and round me rings The mu - sic of the spheres.
morn - ing light, the lil - y white De - clare their Mak- er's praise.
though the wrong seems oft so strong, God is the Rul - er yet.

This is my Fa - ther's world, I rest me in the thought Of
This is my Fa - ther's world, He shines in all that's fair; In the
This is my Fa - ther's world, The bat - tle is not done; Je -

rocks and trees, of skies and seas; His hand the won - ders wrought.
rust - ling grass I hear Him pass, He speaks to me ev - 'ry-where.
sus who died shall be sat - is - fied, And earth and heav - en be one.

WORDS: Maltbie D. Babcock, 1858-1901
MUSIC: Franklin L. Sheppard, 1852-1930

TERRA PATRIS
6.6.8.6.D.(S.M.D.)

This tune in a lower key, No. 529.

DUGAN'S BOY

A remembrance for father and son

I buried my father last week, halfway up an Appalachian hillside, un-der a canopy of cloudless blue sky, virgin-white dogwood blossoms and a dozen shades of springtime Smoky Mountain green. The mourn-ers on that fine, rare day all commented how serene he looked, despite the cancer that had killed him inch by inch and wrinkle by wrinkle over the past year.

Those of us in the family knew such talk was the almost obligatory kindness of the small-town South, and nothing more. But united in our shared experience, we knew it was true nonetheless. There *was* a contentment written there, big as death, for all of us to know if not to see. The Old Man, with his grade-school education and well-earned reputation for irascibility, had proven Tom Wolfe wrong. He *had* gone home again -- home to the quiet and unchanging mountain town that was everything to him.

I should have found some serenity of my own on such a day, but I didn't. There's supposed to be something more, I kept telling myself -- some sense of grief, or despair, or even simple loneliness. I'd settle for a flicker of a sense of loss. A son is supposed to feel all that and more when the father takes his leave and ushers the adolescent into middle age and presents him with the legacy of his own mortality.

Instead, I felt nothing. I cried my eyes out when my dog died, but I couldn't muster a single tear for the man whose name I bear. The closest I could come to any emotion, good or bad, was maybe just a touch of resentment for all the lost moments of heartfelt intimacy parent and child are supposed to share along the way -- moments of special communion that seemed to exist everywhere in '50s television, but not in our house. But I'd grown accustomed to that resentment long ago, and there wasn't even any disappointment anymore. Not for the lifetime of waiting for acceptance and understanding, even for the last nine months spent in the death watch, listening to the clock on the mantel tick away the last chances for rapprochement.

On that splendid mountain-spring day, I no longer cared. And I suspect few of my siblings did either. We did the ritualistic leave-taking, each with our personalized memories, with barely a word among us. All with something to do, or just out of relief to see it over. Even Mother, whose quiet mountain dignity had been called strength by the outsiders and relief by those in the know, saw no need to drag it out any more. After all, there was a three-hour drive ahead of us. If we left now, we could be home before dark.

I've spent the intervening days trying to understand how it came to be that way. What made my father the way he was, and what made the family react the way it did. More important, what makes me feel like such a spiritual Ishmael. I have no answers, no complete and perfect understanding. Just pieces of a puzzle, a few mental snapshots from a life of limited expectations and limitless disappointments. Maybe understanding will come later, I keep telling myself.

The simple country preacher at the Valley River Baptist Church (Est. 1834, Visitors Always Welcome) was trying to deliver words of comfort to the deeply bereaved family. Cutting through the elongated vowels, he seemed to be saying something about the soul's flight to glory, leaving behind just an empty shell in this world of pain and suffering. Much like a jar fly spins its cocoon, eventually freeing itself to soar to happiness and fulfillment in a completely new form, Brother Garland had cast off his diseased body to walk the streets of gold hale and hardy in the body of Christ.

Unfortunately for the import of the simile, one of the omnipresent common house flies that make a career of backwoods one-room Baptist churches chose that moment to alight on the back of the hand of the dearly departed's almost-adult grandson in the second row. "Granpa?" he asked, sotto voce. The rest of the bereaved, who had been doing combat with the same six-legged fiend from hell throughout an eternity of hymns and prayers and hallelujahs, managed to keep a straight face. But just barely. Outside, at the grave after the service, even Mother laughed -- that rich, hearty, from-the-belly laugh that signals she is content.

He was the baby of the family -- the fourth living child and third boy of a self-ordained Baptist preacher. Father Algia worked his fields during the week and rode the same plow mule from church to church on Sundays in the mountain hollows and river valleys near the Carolina-Tennessee border. He was something of a fixture in the area, a supreme arbiter of right and wrong with no modern-day doubts soiling the vestments of his clear-cut expectations for flock and family.

Here was the stuff of Faulkner. This was a man who could expel his own son and daughter-in-law from church because they violated the fourth commandment by hauling a load of peaches from the Georgia groves on a Sunday, trying to make a nickel to support their fledgling family in the midst of the Depression. Never mind that their special sin was attributable to a Saturday breakdown that left them not just temporarily stranded and poorer than dirt, but as it turned out social outcasts as well.

It was the same man who could watch his pre-school son patiently collect pennies until he saved enough for the reddest wagon in the valley, then use his stentorian voice of God to chastise the offending naif for wasting his money. *Now if you had bought a pig or some chickens or something we could use at home, you might amount to something one day,* Dad would later quote from six decades of memory. Clearly, if warmth and intimacy were learned family traits, their prospects were bleak in the judgmental crucible of Algia's household.

In hindsight, it's not surprising that Algia's boys grew to enjoy an early reputation for something other than their devotion to church and the public peace. There were the midnight rides through hill and dale on the primitive mufflerless two-cycle motorcycle, and the odd brush with the local constabulary, most often following some protracted weekend exposure to an indigenous clear, colorless liquid generally merchandised in used fruit jars. By today's standards, it was pretty tame stuff. For Cherokee County in the 1920s, this was the cutting edge of criminality and debauchery.

Compounding the headlong flight into depravity was the lure of easy money from the local lumber camps and pulp mills. Why finish the ninth grade when you could make fifty cents per day for a lot less work than at home, and with a lot less sermonizing and disparagement to boot. The conventional wisdom accepted that school was a good thing, something valued by the community and all therein, but rarely fully achieved, like clean language and clean underwear. But it bore little resemblance to the real needs and expectations of the young and green with little in the way of prospects outside the mill and the tannery anyway.

Even if there had been real opportunity, it wouldn't have mattered. His philosophy of life was profoundly direct, if not as simple as it appeared on the surface. To Dad, what was, was enough. *Give me things I can touch, things with a beginning and an end. Let me cut down trees, clear brush, tan hides, go from here to there. An honest sweat is* all I need to pay my way. Don't ask me for ideas, or burden me with abstracts with no practical use.

This was hard-core hillbilly country, with simple virtues and simple rules, and Dad loved it.

In those final few weeks Dad was able to move about on his own, he spent a lot of time in the bathroom. A lot of time.

We never could tell if it was because he needed to be in there, or if he found refuge in there, or if in the near-catatonia brought on by the massive morphine doses he had simply forgotten where he was, and why. Eventually, when one of us had to go along to help him down and up and clean him and watch the retching and cold sweats, we had a bit better understanding. But he never said a word of complaint. By the time we started using adult diapers to spare him the effort and pain of movement, he couldn't say anything anyway.

We might have seen strength in that, or stoicism, or maybe courage, if we had looked hard enough. By universal acclaim, however, our lasting image was our puritanical Old Man waddling down the hall from bath to bed late one night, his stringy skeleton arm extended and locked in front of him, with undershorts drooping precariously from between thumb and forefinger, his bare bottom shining alabaster white beneath his pajama tops. For some reason, we all found that very, very funny.

My father wasn't a particularly nice man. And there are quite a few acquaintances from his 75 years who wouldn't be even that charitable.

Ask most any of the neighbors of his final years about Garland, and the response generally included the words weird or strange, or maybe even mean and spiteful, or something to that effect. Most of the family would use them as well, especially in the last half of his life, and with increasing frequency as he grew older.

When one of the periodic feuds with the neighbor who owned the adjacent trailer park grew particularly intense, he entered the realm of local legend by following the neighbor to work as a bulldozer operator for days and simply watching him, visibly, from afar, motionless for hours. When he started taking an empty, broken shotgun along for company on these psychological sorties, the neighbor elected to relocate the offending park entrance.

But he could be petty, and vindictive, and purposefully cruel as well, and it was this meanness that rests at the heart of my difficulty in coming to terms with his passing. He could cut the tail off the family dog with a penknife on a whim because he thought it would look better that way. He could take delight in denigrating the kids in front of his cronies, and any other public, for that matter. His pet nickname for his only daughter was the first name of the village simpleton. He never understood why it made her cry, or seemed to care that she did.

His displays of temper and moodiness made visits from outsiders impossible at home and laid the groundwork for a lifetime of resentment between him and Mother. One legendary outburst forced my older brother out of the house on the second day of his three-day leave from the Navy. Buddy died hours later in an early-morning car crash near the Virginia border, on his way back to ship in Norfolk. And when he died, there wasn't a battleship big enough to hold Dad's grief and tears, nor a sea line long enough to bridge the chasm between him and his wife of a quarter-century. It didn't stop the ridicule, or the sporadic tantrums, or the exuberant corporal punishment, either.

The great debate within the family was and continues to be whether he was that way on purpose, with malice aforethought, or as a result of some strange compulsion and basic unhappiness with his lot in life. The differing schools of thought were drawn up along twin-generational lines. The older children tended to discount what they saw as his eccentricities. The younger were less kind. Dad was a very different man to his children of the mountains and his children of the flatland city.

During his last few months, Dad's normal preoccupations turned into obsessions. His ever-present pocketknife became a universal fix-all tool for anything and everything in the house. For some reason, time pieces were a favorite target.

The antique pendulum clock that had kept perfect time since 1890 suddenly seemed to be running fast and required adjustments only he could make with his precision crafting tool. His brand-new wristwatch faced a similar fate. His hands stayed constantly busy.

When he could no longer grasp the knife, he simply wrung his hands in a perpetual washing pantomime. Finally, Mother had to give him a small, fuzzy scrap of cloth, the color of gold, which he kneaded and tugged and folded and stretched long into the night. At the end, those hands callused by a lifetime of much tougher work seemed to be the only part of his body that hadn't been eaten away by the voracious cancer. They were a giant's hands, incongruously attached to his emaciated, childlike form.

Food seemed another manifestation of his frustrations. For his entire life, food had been a fuel, and nothing more. Simple fare, mostly. The fresh vegetables and home-baked bread of his childhood were the staples of our family's table, and he rarely ate meat, except for the odd bit of chicken or his beloved game from the hills.

But in those final months, strange tastes emerged, and he became a fixture at the local supermarkets, paddling about the aisles in the endless search for the satisfying and the exotic. One day it was can after can of Vienna sausages, the next fresh oysters. A couple of times he tossed caution to the wind and actually crossed the heretofore sacrosanct border between real food and ethnic cuisine by zeroing in on canned Chef Boy-Ar-Dee spaghetti.

These forays soon became more Chaplinesque than Chaplin. At least they were to the teenage checkers at the Fresh Air Supermarket. Insulated from care in their adolescent immortality, they giggled and snickered and finally guffawed openly to see this ancient scarecrow shuffling about the store in baggy pants and oversized flannel shirt, an ancient fedora perched as precariously as Absolam's crown on a head made bald by chemotherapy. To them, it continued to be funny right up till his final weeks, when immobility unfortunately cancelled his feature performances.

I wonder who's entertaining them now? And I wonder why their insensitivity made me glow inwardly with anger, while my own produced no emotion at all.

We kids had always known that Mom and Dad had two lives. We were living proof of it -- two separate and distinct families, distanced by decades and differing memories of family life. Two families, drawn apart by different views of the same father, and yet drawn closely together again by our puzzlement over who he really was and what he meant to us.

They were married at 16, at the beginning of the Depression. They didn't know it was a depression, of course. Life in the Appalachian mountain town of Andrews was pretty much catch-as-catch-can all the time. The old-timers will still tell you that no one knew about the so-called Great Depression until 1931, when some Yankee made a wrong turn on the road to Atlanta and casually mentioned it during a stop for gas and directions.

Garland and Carlee started out pretty much like everyone else did -- moving into a one-room shack in a small mountain hollow about a quarter-mile off the Pisgah Road. Dad and friends set about building their first house a few yards away, and at night began the task of producing the first four of the seven kids.

These were the mountain kids -- three boys and a baby girl. My two younger brothers and I weren't to arrive for another two decades, after the first crew had pretty much grown up and left. We were the product of the flatland city living that was Mother's dream -- her escape, and Dad's exile.

The kids of the '30s grew up in a different era, in a different world, and with a different Dad. There were acres of mountain woods in all directions -- seemingly endless green towers for Tarzan ropes, Errol Flynn ramparts and Gene Autry rescues. A small stream ran in front of the house and down the hollow, making vehicular access impossible for the faint of automotive heart, and insulating the place from the surly intrusions of the outside world.

The house was a haven, not just for the West kids, but all the rest of the ragged, overall-clad urchins bred in those woods. It was, as my sister liked to recall, the kind of place everyone in school wanted to visit, and to stay over, and to live. The extended mountain family in those days took in far more than genetics dictated.

Part of what made it so appealing was Mother. Barely older than her children, she was what the natives liked to call a "sport." In local parlance, that meant she didn't feel constrained to observe the social proprieties and unwritten community codes as devoutly as most. That and her general sense of independence cast her as an outsider to native traditionalists, including many of Dad's family. But such an independent attitude also cast a spell over many kids then, as it would today. She knew them, and she spoke their language. She understood their wants and their fears and their longings and their special need for acceptance and toleration. She was almost one of them -- a prematurely gray benefactress content to let them swing from trees, bay at the moon and slay their imaginary dragons without arbitrary rules and without spoken or silent judgment on their childfulness.

Dad wasn't around very much, as my siblings would later recall. He had his diversions, and most of them weren't all that appealing to Mother. But he also worked hard, and he provided. Whether it was clearing brush for power line rights-of-way for the CCC or hauling pulpwood for the local mill in a cousin's rickety Model-T truck, Dad was happy, and he not only tolerated the prehistoric day-care center but also provided the means that made it possible. All in all, it was an arrangement acceptable to everyone. But nothing lasts forever.

We had a couple of hours to kill that afternoon between our arrival at the Best Western motel and the family viewing at the funeral home. My sister wasn't keen on the idea, but she finally agreed to serve as tour guide for the old homestead for me and one of my younger brothers. Mother declined to go, saying sweetly that she didn't particularly care to see the place ever again.

We drove out the Pisgah Road and found the old pathway still in place. There was still no crossing for the stream that guarded the homestead's entrance. But the footbridge that had borne the steps of the four school-bound West kids was there, if a bit smaller than my sister had recalled.

As we hiked up the wooded incline to the home site, we knew the house wouldn't be there. It had burned long ago, as legend has it when some renter grew careless with the copper tubing and turned the clapboard frame and everything it enclosed into cinders. But my sister could still point out all the favorite spots where she competed with her three older brothers as they pummeled a deciduous Tojo and an ever-green Hitler with rocks on their daily war-time trek to school.

Huffing and puffing from the exertion of the climb -- not to mention the two-pack-a-day habit, one cancer operation and a mild heart attack -- she also could still identify the slight rise above the path where Dad used to park his ancient pick-up. Most poignantly, she also could find the precise location where Dad had tethered a spotted pony named Princess for Buddy to find one early morning. Years later, after burying Buddy in the family plot barely two miles away, Dad would spend a week of hard detective work and miles of over-the-road money tracking down that same pony. No one really understood why.

On this day, we could still see the concrete steps on one side of the stream and make out the border of flowers that had lined the walkway to the high and wickedly dangerous front porch. The old root cellar was still visible, though nothing else related to the house was still there. Someone had recently dammed the stream in an attempt to create a pond in the hollow's floor, with some success. The best swinging tree was long gone, it appeared, but several prospects had emerged as worthy replacements, lacking only the rope and old tire, and a new generation of innocents.

A distant cousin would later opine that the ancient stream had insulated the old homestead from the hordes of Floridians currently buying up local mountain parcels as summertime escapes. Since no one could get modern equipment up the rugged terrain to do construction, that whole side of the mountain was safe. Well, sort of safe. The parcel had been purchased recently by the local dentist, who probably would entertain an offer if we were really interested. True to form, we could come to no agreement if we were or not.

I'm not exactly sure when Mother delivered her ultimatum. It was sometime in the late '40s, when the kids stood poised on the verge of not being kids anymore. Mountain hollows and rustic simplicity are fine for children. But her kids were going to have something more than pulp mills and tanneries in their future, she decided, and that something wasn't to be found on the Pisgah Road.

I'm even less sure why Dad went along with it. Maybe it was the sense of adventure and something new. More likely, he figured it would be a temporary thing, easily reversed when the novelty had worn off. He sadly underestimated the strength of Mother's resolve.

The new home was in the bustling metropolis of Winston-Salem. The move gave Dad the chance to start a new life of his own as well. The life-long fascination with things mechanical -- especially vehicles -- translated into formal training in the noble blue-collar profession of trucking. Moving 18-wheelers over the open road appealed to Dad, and he took to it with a passion that lasted to his final days. No doubt, the relocation was a turning point in both his life and Mother's. I suspect neither realized at the time that it wasn't necessarily as much a change for the better as they may have hoped.

At first, life seemed grand. They had a comfortable home. Mother had the great expectations she wanted for her kids. Dad's regular run for the truck line took him twice a week from Winston to Chattanooga -- meaning he had to pass through his beloved Cherokee County regularly. Things seemed so good that after a twelve-year sabbatical they even embarked on a second career as parents, producing me and my two younger brothers within a span of six years.

The night it all ended is one of my earliest memories. A night-time phone call, a lot of noise, Mother in tears, the neighbors ambling about the house in pajamas. It's all jumbled in my memory, just a series of mental pictures really. But it's there. I also remember standing graveside at Buddy's funeral. I can no longer be sure, knowing what I know today, but I also seem to recall asking myself why Mother and Dad weren't sitting together the way they always did.

Things changed after that. Dad wanted to pull up stakes from this cruel and alien world and go back home to the hills. Mother flatly refused. Whether it was spite over Buddy or her long-simmering resentment of what she perceived to be her second-class status among the mountain folk, she never made clear. For whatever reason of his own, Dad seemed to be on the road even more than usual after that, off on ever-longer and more distant trips.

Within only a few years of Buddy's death, he had another chance to make his plea. Dad was asleep when his partner rolled the rig off the mountain road. He could have been killed, he liked to tell everyone later, and was actually pretty lucky to come out of it with only a broken back.

It was during his long convalescence that he hit upon the idea of rejecting the usual insurance settlement and staking himself to a triumphal return home from a can't-miss suit against the truck line. When his white-hot dream ran up against the cold reality of a weak case and a strong opposing attorney, he in typical fashion wound up with nothing. We moved around a bit after that, looking for just the right place in a series of homes, each needing paint just a little more than the last. But never back to the hills. As unchanging as the sunrise and as chilly as the dawn, Mother steadfastly refused to even consider a return there.

During the long ride home after the service, I couldn't help but wonder why he didn't just pick up and go home on his own. In retrospect, it's obvious he was only really happy on his own native soil and truly miserable anywhere else. Did he lack the courage to do it? Not at all. More likely, it was his sense of propriety, or duty, or both. Families don't split in that world, and Mother would not be moved. Stalemate.

I also couldn't help but think how different it all might have been if we had gone back. Could a more serene man have been a better father? Or would we just have traded one discontented parent for another? And what sort of life would we kids have made for ourselves here? Or would the unsettled family life have forced us out of there just as easily as it did in Winston?

Three hours on the road wasn't enough to sort it out. Besides, the questions really didn't deserve that much attention anymore.

A poet would say Dad's downward gyre really began after his accident. Out of his job and rejected in his appeal to go back to the mountain life, he tried his hand at gypsy trucking. He had no head for business of that sort, of course. So what he lacked in business sense, he tried to make up for in sheer hard work, which in trucking meant little more than days and sometimes weeks behind the wheel on the open road. To make that possible sometimes required a bit of pharmaceutical support, which neither sat well with Mother nor made for particularly constructive contacts between father and noisy, energetic children when he returned home to reconstruct his central nervous system.

In the end, of course, he lost it all. The last years of his working life were spent in a series of small jobs for small people for small money and small appreciation. He came full circle from his mountain beginnings. Several people at the memorial service who had known dad for his entire life made essentially that point during the course of the long-soft evening. But it was his older brother who made the off-hand comment that seemed most apt to me: He always seemed to be looking for something, and he never really knew what it was. Maybe the Lord will help him find it now.

For anyone who doubts the ultimate irony of life, consider that Dad's first inkling something was wrong came while driving a semi truck at the age of 74. He'd been asked to ferry a bobcat semi -- a truck without a trailer -- from the neighboring burg to the local headquarters of a truck line, for some minor repair, as I recall. It was more of a favor to a friend than anything else, and it involved little more than an hour's drive down Interstate 40.

Dad had to stop on the side of the road on that trip to throw up. When he announced that, everyone should have known immediately that something was wrong. Very wrong.

Dad's idea of a perfect vacation was nine states in three days. Each trip was an opportunity for discovery -- of some new shortcut, or of even better mileage per gallon. I won't begin to discuss his philosophy on the proper relationship between children and rest stops, and the role played by Nehi bottles in that scheme. When Dad said he had to pull over while driving, we should have taken note.

As it turned out, the stomach cancer by that time was far too advanced to do anything about it anyway. The surgeon opened him up, took a look, stitched him closed and advised the family to take him home and enjoy his last six to eight weeks as best they could. Upon getting the word first hand, Dad decided that wasn't long enough. So he lasted nine months more, just to show everyone who really was in charge. But the cancer, ever to have the last laugh, in the end left him unable to take even a single bite, while it feasted without surcease.

During all his trials and tribulations, and right up till the end of his life, Dad's greatest joy and only real recreation was an occasional solo journey back to his mountain home. Memorial Day was a favorite excuse for a trip, and it had a routine as unchanging as his guilt.

The first order of business was the maintenance of Buddy's grave -- pulling legions of weeds by hand, trimming the boxwood shrubs, and sending a few more tears down the familiar and well-traveled lines of his face to wash the marble headstone. Then a ritual round of official visits to family and friends, followed by a purposefully short night on his older brother's spare bed. By weekend's close, it was back on the road to our house, where the physical fatigue of the journey was exceeded only by the equally debilitating recognition of the ever-diminishing circle of his generation. Those passings, however, were a blessing as well as a curse. After all, funerals for distant cousins, old church members and friends of friends did provide nice excuses to drop everything for one more trip west.

The highlight of the homecoming cycle, of course, was the annual family reunion. That required literally days of preparation and weeks of anticipation, like a kid waiting for Christmas. He'd return from these events full of news about Cora's operation and Glestia's daughter's library certification and Vic's sale of that bottomland prone to spring floods to some gullible Yankee. Every trip produced the miniscule milestones of life reached by cousins and aunts and neighbors and workmates never known to any of us younger kids. But we listened, full of the knowledge of the even longer and more painful history lectures we would receive if we ever evidenced any glimmer of ignorance or, worse yet, real interest. Somewhere in time and space, maybe deep within my subconscious, there is a vast ocean of oral history regarding people I've never really known.

I'm told his farewell appearance at last fall's reunion was exceptionally impressive. My younger brother made up a special bed in his van for Dad and drove him slowly through the scarlets and golds of Soco Mountain and the sunshine and shadow of Nantahala Gorge for one last visit.

He sat propped in a chair at the picnic, Barry reports, receiving visitors in the finest patriarchal style. He even had a few words at the Sunday church service in which he told everyone this would probably be his last reunion, in this world at least, and begging their pardon for any slights real or imagined over the course of his threescore and fifteen. The family remains divided over whether it was a noble and classy gesture, or an Oscar-winning performance.

Unfortunately for both of us, my father and I were profoundly different people, with different values, beliefs, interests and abilities. The man of action and vitality could never understand how he wound up with such a withdrawn and bookish child. Dad asked 'how' of life, and I asked 'why,' and the difference only grew larger as we both matured.

Lord knows he tried to make things different. My complete and utter inability to make the broken lawnmower run or to master the fine art of automotive mechanics or to fathom the mysteries of garden agronomy only drove him into fits of exasperation and occasional rage. Nothing I could do, as hard as I might try, seemed capable of pleasing him. And the more I failed, the more resolute were his efforts to set me straight. It was a vicious, vicious circle.

When he reached his saturation level of bumbling incompetence, the likely result was a quick and vengeful slash with a strap, followed by verbal tirades eloquently chronicling the inadequacies of the new generation and its high priest, his idiot son. When the beatings stopped producing the desired effect, he polished the disappointment speech into a Churchillian masterpiece that cut far deeper than the leather belt. And he knew it.

I've often wondered what might have happened if the local red-brick schoolhouse hadn't been around. It filled a role for me far beyond simple learning. It was a haven and a home, full of acceptance and encouragement. It wasn't that I was particularly bright, mind you. But competition among the 89 blue-collar offspring populating the Hildebran School really wasn't all that intense. And, God bless them, the few lost souls who actually gave a damn in their roles as teachers there seemed eager to embrace someone who actually enjoyed the educational process.

In that world, enthusiasm and diligence -- not necessarily intelligence -- were enough to bring the praise and sense of accomplishment I so desperately wanted. The more it offered, the more I took. After a while, I decided I really didn't need Dad anyway.

This heretical view of education as a source of self-esteem puzzled and confounded Dad even more than my ineptness in the practical aspects of his existence. Schooling was an abstract for him, and a fuzzy one at that. He knew it was supposed to be a good and worthy thing, but how it actually applied to his situation was never quite clearly defined in his philosophy.

I'll also admit that doing well in school gave me no small amount of pleasure, if only to see him wrestle with how to deal with it. Armed with the savings from three years of summer and after-school work, and a letter guaranteeing a student loan, I announced my departure for college on a late-August Sunday afternoon. And when I did, I think both Dad and I knew it meant I had graduated from something more than high school. It was six, maybe seven years before I went home again.

In effect, I chose to run rather than to fight any more. After college came the Army, then grad school and the beginnings of a career. My sister finally engineered the circumstances that brought me and my wife back to their dinner table. Mother was warm and unchanging, Dad polite, wary and almost formal. We had re-established the familial bond, in a manner of speaking, but on very different terms. Over the following years, I carefully parceled out my returns home into two-hour visits -- about the maximum either of us could endure -- generally in presidential-election years.

When he got sick, I was living in London, doing my best to rise up the corporate ladder. My sister called with the news, and I spent several days digesting it, trying to figure out how I felt. My first reaction was pure surprise. It's not that I thought he would live forever, or anything like that. But his family was renowned for its longevity. By my reckoning, the news of his impending demise was about twenty years premature.

But to my shame, that thought passed almost instantaneously, superseded by a sense of relief to be an ocean away. I was glad not to have to watch the day-to-day dying, and all that went with it. That bleak task fell to all the other siblings, who had foolishly chosen to live so close to home. But stronger still, I was glad that I would not be forced to act out the scenes of remorse and regret regarding his impending departure, as if there was some great longing to set things right. I stayed away, and I was glad. Whatever the Old Man and I had to say to each other had been or should have been said long ago.

I visited a couple of times in the final months, mainly because Mother expected it. Dad and I talked baseball some, politics a lot. But we never said anything two strangers trapped in an elevator wouldn't say to each other. We'd never had practice with anything more substantive.

The real troopers were the other kids. I was the visitor, the interloper in the process. And I didn't mind in the least.

My younger brother, the Vietnam-hardened Marine veteran, took the news of Dad's cancer probably worse than any of the other siblings. I'm not sure why. Dad certainly seemed to treat him no less maliciously than any of the rest of us. And as kids, Barry was just as independent and just as anxious to get the hell out as soon as we had finished school or the service would have us or some local Lolita would whisk us away to marital bliss among the trailer homes of the mill-town South.

So I was a bit surprised to see Barry pulling more than his load in caring for the dying man. He carried him like a baby from room to room in the end, and for months sat anxiously poised on the edge of his chair listening to Dad's increasingly incoherent ramblings. It was almost as if he were waiting for something to be said, some words of atonement or explanation, an expiation that would make all the pains and outrages and disappointments of the past understandable, if not all right. Most of the siblings seemed to hope for the same thing, but didn't really expect it. But there was a desperation about Barry, a longing that unfortunately was never satisfied. But at least he had the longing, and the humanity it evidenced. He even cried when Dad finally died.

The end came at home, on a Saturday, at 2:55 in the afternoon. Somewhere in the background an early-season baseball game droned on, where Dad could hear it as he lay on the couch in the living room. The intervals between Dad's slow but regular breathing grew longer and longer, until the interval became eternity.

As deaths go, it actually was quite merciful. The process of getting to that point was sheer hell, of course. But then that's life.

We had argued about putting him back into the hospital in those final days, despite his frequent private pleas to Mother never to see that place again. We wanted to ease the strain on Mother more than anything else. He certainly wouldn't have known where he was. But

Mother said no. He wanted to be at home, and home is where he will be, she said quietly but firmly. Nor was she keen to allow the outside services to come in. We are family, she said, and family takes care of family. Not all of us agreed, but we all kept our peace.

At the memorial service the night before the funeral, all Dad's cronies turned out to pay their respects. Most of them evoked the old man in an eerie sort of way. Maybe it was the way they carried themselves. Maybe it was the weathered, worn and weary look that marked their six and seven-plus decades of Appalachian mountain life.

These were men and women who also had come of age in the Great Depression in the belly of Appalachia. They knew poverty as something much, much more than a statistical calculation, and they knew the hardship that comes from stony ground and no jobs. They knew what it meant to be hungry, and how important it was to share and to pull together. These men and women raised families and instilled values and overcame whatever life threw at them. They endured, and they prevailed, as Faulkner would say.

Since I wasn't one of the mountain kids, most of the mourners weren't quite sure who I was. But I suppose I looked enough like the rest of the family to make the obligatory overture inevitable.

"You're Dugan's boy, aren't you?"

At least 10 people uttered those exact words over the course of the evening. Dugan's boy.

Dugan was his nickname among his closest friends. Oddly enough, no one in the family had any idea where it came from, although we'd heard it used from time to time, especially among the circles of mountain folks. It had just always been there, whenever he interacted with anyone from the old home town.

Some people said it had been given to him by his first boss, after a popular cartoon character of the era. Its origins really didn't matter. What was important was what it meant to Dad. It was his special label, his unique password in the world that had given him birth and defined his own sense of belonging.

Once the familial identity had been established, the people at the visitation service would express their sympathies, invoke the usual religious imagery that made up the fiber of their lives, and then launch into a favorite Dugan story. Most involved some kind of adolescent adventure, or maybe a shared happiness, or even a special kindness Dad had somehow brought about. And true to their code, many also would talk frankly about the disappointments and universal miseries they shared with Dad. The picture they painted added to a puzzle far more complex and contradictory than I had really even known.

"You're Dugan's boy, aren't you?"

Yes, I suppose I am.

It was years before I realized that he was as scared of me as I was of him. I feared his anger from my earliest memory. I hurt and seethed and raged mutely at his taunting, and most of all at his ridicule -- the piercing verbal daggers hurled for humiliation, for not being like him.

It took two decades before I saw through my pain and embarrassment and realized the defensive nature of those outbursts. It was fear of something he didn't understand, flesh and blood with alien values. I was the living manifestation of that part of his life filled with his own disappointment and loneliness. The tragedy, I suppose, is that he couldn't express it any other way, and I couldn't or wouldn't see it earlier.

For the longest time, I bristled at the well-intentioned but subtly insulting words of comfort offered by some at the memorial service. Old Dugan did the best he could.

At first, there was the simmering resentment that came from knowing that simply wasn't true. He didn't do the best he could. God knows, he could have put something aside from a lifetime of hard work and sweat, if not for himself then for his wife of 58 years. He could have been kinder and more supportive. He could have taken the time, just once, to praise, or even to just listen. He could have done a lot better. He could have been more of the father we all wanted so desperately, right up to the end.

But sitting alone in the dark at 4 a.m., with my wife's peaceful breathing from the next room providing a welcome measure of order and calm, that anger begins to fade. Did I ever really know him well enough to decide what was or wasn't his best? For too many years, I took the easy way out with Dad. I hid away in my own pain and anger, withdrawn into the smug judgmentalism that comes so easily after years of living with someone so admittedly and profoundly lacking in the traditional social and familial graces. He was far from perfect, and that makes it too easy to hide in my own disappointments.

But it also leaves me on that Carolina mountainside in an emotional vacuum that scares me more than death itself. Yes, he inflicted emotional scars on all of us -- scars we'll carry to our own mountainside rests. But hate and anger don't make them any easier to bear. They only make them deeper and uglier, and the sense of spiritual isolation only stronger.

Sitting alone late in the night, it seems clearer somehow. I'll never understand the enigma that was my father -- not completely, anyway. He was too complex for that, his demons and my own too numerous and too omnipotent to allow a Solomon's judgment.

Maybe that complete understanding isn't what's important. What's important is that I take that first step to my own salvation and just accept him for what he was -- only a man, with the ample share of weakness and fallibility that entails. If I'm ever going to feel human -- feel the tragedy that comes with losing a father -- I have to first put away the anger.

I can't measure my father anymore by his shortcomings. He certainly thought he did the best he could. And given the forces of light and dark with which he did battle over the years, maybe he did. There will always be someone around to judge and condemn and point out the failings and contradictions. We're all easy targets in that regard. Dad's had enough of Algia's Old Testament judgments, from all the kind-hearted mourners and his own son as well.

In the last few months of his life, Dad had taken all the kids aside and tried to give them each something from the personal treasures accumulated over the years and stored secretly in the cedar chest in his bedroom. For one, it was his collection of old coins gathered from the endless toll lines of over-the-road trucking. For another, it was the hunting rifle borne over countless nameless Carolina hills.

My gift was a silver ballpoint pen, probably bought for a buck in some long-forgotten truck stop, rarely used but nonetheless carried reverentially in the shirt pocket as an instrument of learning and expression.

His real legacy, though came later, after his death. It came in the middle of the night with the recognition that he was right after all. What was, was enough. I can't expect perfect understanding, and I have no right to bestow forgiveness upon him. There's nothing to forgive. I can only accept him for what he was, and in doing so just maybe begin the process of saving myself.

A father can do worse for a son.

THE OLD RUGGED CROSS

1. On a hill far a-way stood an old rug-ged cross, The em-blem of
2. O that old rug-ged cross, so de-spised by the world, Has a won-drous at-
3. In that old rug-ged cross, stained with blood so di-vine, A won-drous
4. To the old rug-ged cross I will ev-er be true, Its shame and re-

suf-f'ring and shame; And I love that old cross where the dear-est and best
trac-tion for me; For the dear Lamb of God left His glo-ry a-bove,
beau-ty I see; For 'twas on that old cross Je-sus suf-fered and died,
proach glad-ly bear; Then He'll call me some day to my home far a-way,

Chorus

For a world of lost sin-ners was slain.
To bear it to dark Cal-va-ry. So I'll cher-ish the old rug-ged
To par-don and sanc-ti-fy me. So I'll cher-ish the cross, the
Where His glo-ry for-ev-er I'll share.

cross, Till my tro-phies at last I lay down; I will cling to the
old rug-ged cross,

old rug-ged cross, And ex-change it some day for a crown.
cross, the old rug-ged cross,

WORDS AND MUSIC BY GEORGE BENNARD

THE CROSS WE BEAR

On the burden of caring

The finest man I ever knew is gone, and much as I wish otherwise, he isn't coming back. Not today, and not tomorrow. Not soon, or someday. Not ever.

The news bulletins and official reports say he died in a drowning accident, in the river he loved near the spot where his new dream home was being built. Drowning may be the official cause of death, but it really was more a matter of his being overweight. Not corpulent, mind you, though he had indeed long ago lost his boyish athletic physique. The real reason for his premature passing rested in the heavy burden of concern and responsibility he felt for all his 59 years, for a list of family, friends, neighbors, even passing acquaintances and complete strangers. Caring was his burden, his cross to bear -- and caring too much killed him.

John was the most amazing mix of capabilities and attributes of anyone I've encountered over my span of years. He possessed a keen intellect and quick mind, as all his degrees and honors and accolades attested. But what carried him to a different, higher level than the other smart people I've known was an uncanny self-discipline that he applied to learning and life. John brought a focus and a drive to know and understand everything, and to see things through no matter what, that left all the rest of us far, far behind. If anyone on this earth can be said to have made the most of his gifts, it was him.

Not that he was perfect. His huge intellect was matched by an equally large bull-headedness. He studied every matter in intricate detail – every fact, every nuance, every complication and special circumstance, and every possibility and conceivable option. But when he arrived at his opinion or conclusion or decision, it was immutable, carved in stone.

Add to that a mountain pride that made him lock away his own troubles and pain and frustrations behind a stoic façade, and the opening lines of a prescription for an early and untimely death were already in place. It was his special cross to bear. And bear it he did. Right up to the moment it killed him.

But what took John into a very special realm of exceptionality were the values he layered on his intellect, like rich, sweet icing on cake. No one I know ever matched his genuine desire to help others -- to provide the help that made things better if not all right immediately, and to have the insights and understanding that somehow unlocked a solution to the larger issues inevitably beneath every dire circumstance or emergency.

Over the years, I saw him deliver on that promise to others more times than I can count, for the powerless and pained, for those with special needs and seemingly insurmountable problems, for personal burdens large and small.

Legal advice, and tons more practical common-sense counsel on day-to-day calamities. Time and energy on everyday matters for neighbors and acquaintances, from helping repair a damaged roof to replacing worn-out brakes, or bringing in a field of hay before the heavens opened, in his weekend finery of ragged jeans and a sweat-stained tee shirt. Waived legal fees and financial hand-outs, large and small, for the major and minor disasters that always seemed to befall the affluent and needy alike (but far more so the needy). Sometimes just by being there for someone, saying little or even nothing, a calm source of supreme faith and hope.

Listing all the ways he found to help those around him is a fool's errand. There's just no way to count all of them delivered over the years, or to describe how vast the range of problems he helped solve, trivial and profound. What was trivial and what was profound, of course, depended then as now on your point of view. For John, very little of what vexed others or caused any degree of pain or form of anguish was trivial.

Given his beneficent nature, it's little wonder that he was such a poor businessman, or that the vast riches that normally flow so easily for other Phi Beta Kappas and Summa Cum Laudes and Tops of Their Class seemed to elude him throughout his life. He passed on the chance to take the corner-office jobs with the big firms in Washington and Atlanta and even Charlotte, preferring instead to hang out a law shingle in his home town, "where I can do the most good," as he explained matter of factly, without any hint of guile or pretense.

Doing the most good never appeared to pay all that well. But he did it anyway, day after day and year after year, till the years finally ran out.

I won't presume to say I was John's best friend. John had dozens, more likely hundreds, of best friends… long, long lists of people who didn't just take of his time or knowledge or even his money, but took of him. He made every person feel special, as if some unique personal connection existed. Men and women alike wanted to share his company, just to bathe in the warm glow of serenity that seemed so easy to find in his presence.

I'm sure we shared a special bond that lasted throughout the years, despite long periods of distance and distraction.

We could go for months, even years, of separation while I chased a career and he did his good deeds, and then meet again and pick up a suspended conversation precisely where it left off. We shared the same sense of humor and would constantly seek to beat each other to the punch line in any joke. He was the best man in my wedding, and my designated driver on the day I got my draft notice during the Vietnam war.

We vroomed around Scotland together a couple of times while I lived in England, marveling at our survival after driving so long on the wrong side of the road. We guffawed at our faux sophistication in sharing the same critical view of a modernist production of The Tempest at the National Theatre on the banks of the Thames.

He used my cramped New York City apartment as a base during one annual summer holiday for showing his family the Big Apple, or at least as much of it as they could stomach, and afford. We had a much more enjoyable time crabbing in the surf and tide pools at the Outer Banks in our underwear, or despairing in front of his television every Saturday during the glorious mountain autumns at the futility of our alma mater's football follies. We could sit for hours on any weekend, in any season, saying next to nothing, but speaking volumes.

All that, and so many more memories. So very many more.

I may not have been *his* best friend, but he certainly was *mine*.

Friends like me and family alike competed for his time, for the opportunity to be with him. Just hanging out with John seemed to convey a sense of well-being and contentment – a calm knowledge that his presence meant someone was there to help, someone who genuinely cared, and someone with the intellect and commitment to make it better, no matter what "it' happened to be – a legal problem, a money problem, a hiccup in worldly relationships, maybe even a simple sense that someone likes me and values me and cares about me. "It" can cover a whole lot of ground in this world.

That sort of profound ability to connect with so many people, no matter how diverse in background or circumstance, had its own particular dark side, though. The competition for his time and attention was sometimes fierce and occasionally ugly. Part of his gift was an apparent ability to balance those often antagonistic demands with equanimity and grace. At least, it seemed that way to the outside eye. Who knows, now, what it was really doing to him on the inside.

He was a special, special man, and we all saw it and treasured it. And probably abused it, right up to the moment he died.

In the final few years of his life, John changed. It was as clearly to be seen as God's own sunshine, or the Devil's darkness. And we all remarked on it to each other. But we did nothing. John was strong. John was smart. John could do anything. Except save himself, it turned out.

Maybe it was the pressure of so many people asking so much for so long. A mutual friend once dared to speak the unspoken truth. "John can't say no to anybody," he observed, "even when he should."

He had progressed from simple country lawyer to distinguished member of the bench, with all the rights and perquisites that came with it. But to John, his judgeship wasn't an opportunity to sit back at long last and enjoy his well-earned prominence and position. It was just another venue – a bigger, more powerful tool -- for fulfilling his real purpose in life, which was still first and foremost helping others, only now from behind the bench instead of in front of it. Outside the court, the calendar of personal small-town things to do for others never shrank, either. If anything, it only grew more crowded. The only thing that didn't seem to grow was the number of hours in a day, or the number of days in a week. Or the number of days left in his life.

But at the end, John was indeed a changed man. More and more often he was seen alone – eating a silent meal, slowly pacing the sidewalks around the city square, ambling along the banks of his beloved Catawba River. He rarely seemed to smile anymore, and his look was frequently downcast, as if lost in distant thought, or maybe even melancholy. His small talk grew more clipped and superficial, and more and more phone calls simply went unreturned. An important man, we all thought. A busy man, we all hoped. A burdened man, we failed to appreciate.

The last time I saw John, he was gaunt, drawn, moving lethargically, with a hobble far too pronounced for his years, eyes dull and distant. You look like hell, I said, as would any true friend to another in similar circumstances. I feel like it, too, he replied. Must be the flu. Just can't seem to shake it.

Less than a week later, he was dead.

Friends try to assuage the pain by pointing out all the memories left behind, and the legacy that lives as long as any of us who knew him are here to tell the story of a great man. But memories and a legacy of old, old stories are no comfort to me. He's gone. Forever. And I'm still here to know that. Call it my cross to bear.

My cross is knowing I'll never again feel the simple pleasure that came from being around John. Or the comfort I took in knowing he was my friend, my sage counsel, my confidante, my confessor. We'll never have the opportunity to add to the memories, with new experiences, new ideas, new problems, new answers to life's mysteries large and small. I resent the loss of a longer, richer, fuller future together that we'll never have now that he is gone. The past is the past, and for me, the past is not enough. Not when life still could be – *should be* -- lived in the company of a man like John.

And I also resent the waiting. Mortality is tough enough to accept as a concept, more so as an inevitability. The knowledge of my own mortality is a bitch. But waiting for the inescapable end while still caring so very, very much for someone forever lost may be an even bigger one. I'm not sure it's a cross I can bear. But I suppose I'll have to. I only wish John were here to tell me how.

Lord, I Want to Be a Christian

1. Lord, I want to be a Chris-tian in my heart, in my heart,
2. Lord, I want to be more lov - ing in my heart, in my heart,
3. Lord, I want to be more ho - ly in my heart, in my heart,
4. Lord, I want to be like Je - sus in my heart, in my heart,

Lord, I want to be a Chris-tian in my heart.
Lord, I want to be more lov - ing in my heart.
Lord, I want to be more ho - ly in my heart.
Lord, I want to be like Je - sus in my heart.

In my heart, in my heart,
in my heart, in my heart,

Lord, I want to be a Chris-tian in my heart.
Lord, I want to be more lov - ing in my heart.
Lord, I want to be more ho - ly in my heart.
Lord, I want to be like Je - sus in my heart.

WORDS: African-American spiritual; adapt. John W. Work, Jr., and
       Frederick J. Work, 1907
MUSIC: African-American spiritual; adapt. Frederick J. Work, 1907

I WANT TO BE A CHRISTIAN
Irregular

GOD DAMNED

Threats of hell and hopes of paradise

I'll be god-damned.

I've heard those words off and on my entire life, and from virtually every stratum of the society in which I live.

Most often, they're a common interjection – an exclamatory term, expressing emotion. And they're remarkably versatile, conveying a multitude of moods, appropriate to an exceptional range of situations and circumstances.

Depending on the intonation, they can be used to express wonderment and amazement... frustration and despair... even surprise and elation.

But I can't recall ever hearing them used literally. That is, I hadn't until I heard myself say them last week when my older brother died. At that moment, I realized that God has indeed damned me. Why, I don't know. I just know that He has.

That blinding insight really took root a few weeks earlier, when Bill called to let me know the diagnosis. Ever the practical-minded, logic-driven engineer, he recounted the various places the cancer had been detected, and the various matters of business that he needed to tie up in the time allotted to him by the doctors who decide such things.

But what stood out in the conversation wasn't the news itself. After all, this was just the latest installment in our family's litany of death passages. Cancer runs through our family like – well, like cancer. We'd all already had far too much experience coming to grips with this final rite of passage. In what's left of this family, we know the death-watch drill. We don't need any Elizabeth Kubler Ross, thank you very much.

No, what made that conversation so moving was the quiet grace and equanimity with which he spoke the death sentence. Like his mother and father and sister and brother before him, Bill accepted the inevitability of the situation – no, more than accepted it, almost embraced it in a way that still takes my breath away, and replaces it with a vacuum of personal despair.

You see, Bill and those who preceded him into the great beyond went with a profound belief that they were simply moving on to something more. Death was a transition, a step into something new and better. These are people who have faith – real faith – in something bigger, some master plan in which all the senseless aspects of life at long last make sense. They have faith in God.

And I don't.

It's not that I don't want to have faith. I've spent too many sleepless nights, staring into the dark, trying to find it somewhere deep within me. I want to believe. I want the comfort, the inner peace, the sense of meaning that all my family members seem to have found with such ease, and such certainty.

I want to believe that there is something more, and that there is something waiting for us that will explain if not atone for all the pain and suffering and cruelties and inequities I've seen in this world.

Some of us just can't accept the simplistic assumption that we poor miserable humans are to blame for all that's wrong with our world, while the flashes of beauty and love and compassion that dot our lives like fireflies on a summer night are evidence of God's love and personal handiwork. If mankind's poor use of free will is to blame for this puzzling mess around us, then God has to accept some responsibility, too. God can't have it both ways.

Maybe the whole idea of free will is really nothing more that some sort of giant teleological test, and the world around us only a giant lab exercise to see if we can make sense out of things without Him. If so, the test is over. The results are in, and they paint a pretty bleak picture.

I've seen humanity in all its inhumanity, the collective consequence of our lauded free will, and I despair for it. We've proven our shortcomings time and time again in places like Cambodia and Rwanda and the Balkans and Mosul and the gulag and death camps and the torture chambers in places too numerous to mention. We see it in the indifference that allows billions to wallow in poverty and hunger amid squalor and disease, while the select few pre-occupy themselves with cell phones and country clubs and just the right couture. We nurture it every day in thousands of callous acts of petty pain and cruel indifference we blithely inflict with impunity on the weak and powerless around us.

Yes, we've shown what we can do when left to our own devices. But why can the faithful see that and use it to make their faith even stronger, when others – like me – see it and find only despair? Why do so many of us see the same sad picture and draw not strength but hunger from it – a desperate longing for answers that never seem to come?

Yes, I want to believe in a just and beneficent God. I want to have faith. So after many deaths and much reflection, I have to conclude that I lack faith not through my own shortcomings as much as God's arbitrary decision to damn me.

The wise men and women I've consulted in matters of spirituality just don't seem to get what I'm talking about. Without exception, they listen patiently and tell me to simply believe – to just keep telling myself over and over again that I have faith.

What a load of hooey. Faith isn't something you simply select, like choosing a new car, or deciding to become a Republican. If you have doubts, you don't have faith. And I've never been able to dispel those doubts.

I look at faith the same way the Supreme Court justice talked about pornography. I may not be able to define it, he said. But I sure know it when I see it.

I'll know faith when I have it. And I just don't have it. No amount of repeating the words aloud or to myself will change that. No, faith comes when the desire to believe meets God's willingness to bestow. Call it grace, call it a blessing, call it what you like. I just know He hasn't seen fit to send it my way.

I'm sick and tired of people throwing Descartes in my face, too. My philosophy prof in college took great delight in explaining faith in terms of Cartesian logic. I believe because it's the best bet. If I believe and there's no God, I've lost nothing. If I believe and there is a God, then I win big.

Sounds like playing craps in Vegas to me. And I seem to recall another pretty bright guy commenting that God doesn't play dice. Well, neither should Christians when it comes to their soul.

No, faith has to be more than logic and pure rationality. Call me a romantic, or a mystic, or even a fool. But to me, faith is a two-way street – a marriage of man's desire and God's grace.

I don't expect God to do all the work, either. I'll do my part. I'll meet Him more than half-way. I don't expect a burning bush or an angelic visitation. All I ask is that He move toward me just a hair. Take a millisecond to grant me just a mustard seed of His grace, and I'll move the mountain for Him. He did it for Paul on the road to Damascus. Please do it for me, too, anywhere you like. Name the place and time and I'll be there. Help me just a bit. Please.

I want what everyone else seems to have found so easily. I want what I heard in Bill's voice, and in the voices of all the others who have passed this way before. Not in what they say, not in the words they use. But in the peace and serenity that bathe their words and the confidence and contentment that lets them live this life without despair and leave this world at peace.

God's grace. That's all I ask. But time is running out for me. With Bill's passing, I'm now the patriarch of the remaining family. The oldest survivor. Next in line to hear the magic words from the modern medical establishment. I'm so much closer to the end than the beginning, the questions grow more important every day, and still the skies are dark and silent.

I guess no one is listening.

I'll be God damned.

Love Lifted Me

MATTHEW 14:29-31
James Rowe, 1912

Howard E. Smith

PUBLIC DOMAIN

LOVE LIFTED ME

Finding the answer within

My wife and I just completed the latest in a series of visits to the local medical providers, in the accelerating round of various tests and procedures and evaluations and consultations that accompany our advancing years.

We try to make the best of it on each visit, and to make light of it when we can. We like to think that the reason every staff member at our family clinic knows us by name is our sparkling personalities rather than our burgeoning medical files. But we both know our visits are a reminder of our mortality, and all the things we have yet to do as responsible adults in the management of our affairs. Sojourns at the clinic and amazingly frequent treks to the pharmacy have fueled a lot of back and forth about the things we still want to do before we're done, including many that involve the people who remain important in our lives.

These truly grown-up conversations have coincided with a fortuitous series of run-ins with long-time friends from different parts of our life – simple, relaxed visits mostly, where we tell old stories, share some laughs, remember old friends and favorite fuzzy companions. And in truth, most of these visits involve some time despairing of the follies of the world round us, and questioning of the puzzling values and priorities of the whipper-snapper generation, which is now anyone under the age of 50. Then we invariably laugh at ourselves, compare our curmudgeonly ways to those of our own parents, and accept if not embrace our new role as the geezer generation.

But as we recently sat on a life-long and treasured friend's back deck in the summer twilight after a fine dinner, it also occurred to me that we weren't just reliving the past, or even dwelling on it, really. We were very much living in the moment, and enjoying everything about it – the opportunity to be together, to exchange thoughts and beliefs, to share a special connection based on a genuine appreciation and acceptance of each other. And as we sat in the gathering dusk, the conversation came so easily and lasted so long. We never seemed to realize how the deepening night slowly enveloped us, and we were totally indifferent to the fact we had become disembodied voices in the dark, still talking and laughing and still expressing wonder and incredulity and delight. Our corporeal selves had faded away into the night, replaced by kindred spirits unburdened by aged earthly substance. But whatever we were, we were still connected enough to be making new memories.

And it struck me like a bolt from above that night, like an illuminating flash cutting through the dark. The dense gray fog of doubt that had enveloped me most of my life was of my own making. Here was the answer I sought to so many of the basic questions that have plagued me throughout life. And it was so simple, really. To be happy and content, you only need to live in the moment, with the people and living beings you care for, grabbing onto the simple joys of everyday life, with both hands.

To steal a thought from one of my favorite stories of all time, Inherit the Wind: Perhaps in my quest to understand my abject lack of faith and my over-abundance of doubt, I looked too deeply into the clouds above and too far beyond the distant horizon. I sought answers from elsewhere and without, when it was right there in front of me all the time, and within me all my life. I just chose not to see it. The secret may lie in the simple four-letter word that makes possible my ability to live in and appreciate every moment I'm blessed to receive. That word is love.

Funny, but not all that long ago this way of thinking about love would have seemed so trite, so schmaltzy and saccharine to me. A tired old cliché, best suited to a Hallmark card, I would have said. Just another four-letter word, tossed about thoughtlessly, with no real meaning.

It's a teenager's passionate promise, and an adult's solemn wedding pledge, both waiting to be broken. My cousin loves fly fishing and the Atlanta Falcons, much like a chubby guy loves his Rocky Road. My sister-in-law loves what we did with the remodeled family room, and especially the drapes. Advertisers tell us to love the feel of the new toilet paper from MegaCorp, and how they are 'lovin' it' at Mickey D's. I grew up on I Love Lucy, and the Love Boat. This one, simple four-letter word has generated books, poems, songs, paintings, sculpture, essays, billet-doux, etchings on bathroom stalls, tattoos and tee shirts, backseat courtships and barroom negotiations, ad campaigns and holy crusades, parking lot fistfights and grand city sieges.

No wonder the word seems so tired and so pedestrian, after centuries of ubiquity in the world around us, and so much over-use in so many diverse contexts. It's the common currency of the shallow and thoughtless, bandied about so carelessly that any real meaning and value had long ago been compromised, if not lost altogether. For me, like so many others, the real depth and power and meaning of the word had been buried under that pile of overuse, its true meaning cheapened and coarsened and diminished. Until that night with friends.

And when the word did take on its real meaning, the message for me within its true depth, meaning and power followed close behind.

Love life, and the people who help you live it. Savor every moment of the time you have, and treasure the people who make it all rich and special and meaningful.

The many feelings and emotions that come with loving people and the world we all collectively create are now so much clearer to me. The incredible highs we still can construct together, and those distinctive bittersweet golden remembrances we will always share, accessible only through memory, but cemented firmly there nonetheless. The special bond that comes from a shared laugh, a mutual tragedy, and a quiet yet heartfelt conversation on matters grand and petty. A shared moment of honest doubt or deepest fear, or of small hopes and great dreams.

Maybe love is not much more than learning to appreciate each and every moment along life's way, and to appreciate and care for all the people who make those moments possible. It's telling someone you care, and then showing them just how much. No, not someone... *everyone*.

You see, in my personal moment of clarity and insight, I also realized that love was even more complex and nuanced than I'd ever realized. It's the unique and profound way I feel about a very special woman. It's the bond I feel with family and old friends. But it also must embrace the willingness to look for something good within every person I meet, and a commitment to cherishing the existence of every creature God has seen fit and worthy of the gift life.

I think of all the bipedal and quadripedal creatures that I've known... the family and friends and acquaintances that have contributed to my life... the love they have given me, and the love they've allowed me to bestow in return... the sheer joy we have shared and the troubles we have endured.

Love also is the quiet happiness that comes from slowly stroking a gently purring kitten rescued from oblivion, or tossing a smelly tennis ball time after time after time for an overgrown and unwanted stray mutt too nondescript or too big or too stupid to win the heart of a prospective parent at the overcrowded shelter. Love is the sheer joy of celebrating every life, whatever the species, in the moment – fully aware of the inevitable counterbalance to all that joy, which comes as the hellish torment of knowing each and every one will only tear your heart to shreds in the end, when they're no longer there to provide the modicum of moment to moment delight that makes the world bright and sunny and full of boundless hope and primal joy.

Real love is a thousand things great and small, but few if any of them should apply to shilling toilet paper. Real love embodies genuine caring and compassion for others. It's wanting to protect and provide for, and to nurture and support, to give and share. It's a commitment to trying to understand and accept, to being truthful and open, to placing one another above the shallow and transitory. It's knowing when to talk and when to listen, and when to forgive and when to forget. It's knowing someone else's doubts and fears, and their hopes and dreams, and being there to help deal with all them in whatever way is wanted or needed. Love is treating all living things with understanding and acceptance, and with respect and dignity. It's all this, and a lot more.

I'm content with the knowledge that I've had others in my life to give it meaning and value. I've been blessed with people and other living beings to love, and with people and companion creatures who I came to know have loved me in return for what I am – a unique combination of debatable strengths and undeniable weaknesses, noble aspirations and selfish imperfections, good intentions and broken promises. I've had the chance to see so much of life, good and bad, along the way, and to see how simple human decency – or lack thereof – plays so large a role in what constitutes the good, and what dictates the bad.

Love's true meaning seems so different to me now. It's a four-letter word, still, but now it's my own special four-letter word. It's the four-letter word I want to come to mind when I think about my life, and what it has been, and what lies ahead. For so long, many other

four-letter words seemed to apply to and define my existential predica-
ment. It's time to make this one four-letter word *mine.*

Call it schmaltz, call it trite. Call it a desperate grab for something
to hang onto in the twilight of life. Call it what you will. All I know
is that it's left me with something I've wanted my whole life… at long
last, the first glimmer of an answer to questions of faith and doubt that
I can not just accept but more importantly embrace.

However you choose to characterize my revelation, I have found
a kind of peace and contentment in it. It may not be the complete
answer to all the questions I've had about life and faith and doubt, but
it's a very nice framework in which to conduct the remaining debate. It
may not work for everyone. It may not be perfect. And I can't say I'm
any closer to my hopes of heaven beyond. But now I am more content
with my place in life – my time right now, here and in this moment.
And I can live with it – certainly a lot better than I ever could without
it. My new-found faith in love won't cure all the world's ills, but it
might cure mine.

You see, maybe the faith I'm after comes from this world as much
as any heavenly intervention. Maybe, just maybe, what I've found is a
first step on the road leading to the complete and transcendent faith
that has been so elusive for so long. And maybe the God's grace I've
always coveted comes less as a blinding flash than a gradual dawn – in-
distinct at first, but eventually bright and beautiful.

Maybe faith begins with the love we find within ourselves that
gives meaning and purpose to each individual life. Maybe love makes
greater faith possible, by providing the only effective immediate anti-
dote to the pain and torments that poison our lives. I'll focus on the
here and now – loving life, and loving others -- and trust in whatever
God may exist to take care of whatever afterlife there may be. Seems
like an equitable split of responsibilities to me. And if I fulfill my part

of the bargain, maybe I'll find that faith in love is the passageway to the kind of greater faith my more spiritual friends and family have found.

It's a lot of maybes, I know. But for the first time in my life, all the 'maybes' are cause for hope and optimism, more than reason for doubt. Through this new-found faith in the idea of love, and in the power of love, I'm lifted above so many of my past doubts and fears – to a place infinitely preferable to the deep, dark pit of abject despair that has imprisoned me far too long. Absent the maybes, I'd be left with no faith at all. I've been there, and it's not pretty or pleasant.

I'm at peace with the kind of faith I have found at long last, at least compared to the confusion and uncertainty that I knew before. I may not have found all the answers, or embraced the precise definition of faith others expound. But I found what works for me. I'm lifted up.

When nothing else could help, love lifted me.

Go Tell It On The Mountain

ABOUT THE AUTHOR

Garland West is a writer and business consultant with several decades experience in the public policy process, most notably matters involving food security, economic development and organizational leadership. Over his career, he has applied his academic training in journalism to coverage of agricultural, environmental and trade policy in Washington and Europe, and has written articles, speeches, issue analysis and commentary on these and other matters for clients that include major corporate leaders and prominent global consulting firms. His resume includes postings in Washington, Minneapolis, London, New York, Chicago and Detroit, both as a corporate executive and president of his own company. He and his wife Nancy today reside deep within in the Blue Ridge Mountains, where they maintain an animal sanctuary and savor a more contemplative and relaxed pace of life.